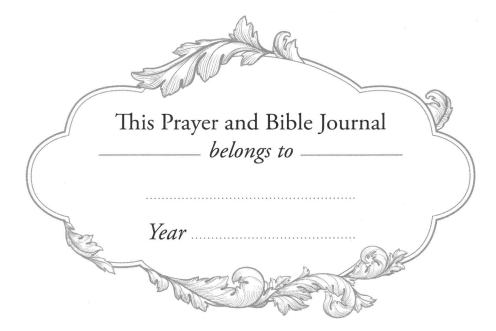

This Prayer and Bible Journal
belongs to

Year

FRANK M. HASEL

LONGING FOR
GOD

A PRAYER AND BIBLE JOURNAL

Pacific Press®
Publishing Association

Nampa, Idaho | Oshawa, Ontario, Canada
www.pacificpress.com

Cover design by Simon Eitzenberger, www.desim.de
Cover design resources from Daxiao Productions/Shutterstock.com
Inside design by Simon Eitzenberger, www.desim.de
Image credits: pp. 20, 21, 42 nature photos/Shutterstock.com; pp. 46, 47, 68 Skreidzeleu/Shutterstock.com; pp. 72, 73, 94 Sundari/Shutterstock.com; pp. 98, 99, 120 Elenamiv/Shutterstock.com; pp. 126, 127, 148 nature photos/Shutterstock.com; pp. 154, 155, 176 Daxiao Productions/Shutterstock.com; pp. 180, 181, 202 Galyna Andrushko/Shutterstock.com; pp. 206, 207, 228 RomoloTavani/Thinkstock.com; pp. 232, 233, 254 Creative Travel Projects/Shutterstock.com; pp. 258, 259, 280 nature photos/ Shutterstock.com; pp. 284, 285, 306 alexnika/Shutterstock.com; pp. 310, 311, 332 Cattallina/Shutterstock.com

Originally published as *Sehnsucht nach Gott: Ein Bibel-Gebets-Tagebuch* © 2012 Frank M. Hasel, Seminar Schloss Bogenhofen. Translated by Susi Mundy.

You can obtain additional copies of this book by calling toll-free 1-800-765-6955 or by visiting http://www.adventistbookcenter.com.

ISBN: 978-0-8163-6336-0

March 2018

IN MEMORY OF

my wonderful marriage partner and friend, Ulrike
(April 30, 1965–October 3, 2009).
With this book I try to continue
what you began and what you practiced.
I think you would be happy to see this book.
Thank you so much for your inspiration
and for modeling what it means to live with Jesus.

This book is dedicated to my fantastic sons

Jonathan,

Florian,

&

Daniel

May you have life-changing encounters with our fascinating God!

CONTENTS

LONGING FOR GOD

CONTENTS

LONGING FOR GOD

PAGE

THANKS

A book like this would not be possible without the active help and support of numerous people.

// A big THANK-YOU goes to Roland Dell'mour for his initial interest in this project and his expertise in formatting the first layout version of the German edition. Thank you, Roland, for countless hours where you have helped without pay so that the book could become a reality. Thank you for setting deadlines and for your patience and great creativity in helping to make my ideas become reality.

// A heartfelt thank-you goes to Simon Eitzenberger for his fantastic work on the layout of this book. You have made the book even better and more attractive. You know how to work with InDesign and what people respond to positively.

// Thank you to the members of the spiritual masterplan team at Bogenhofen Seminary in Austria, Europe, who gave me an opportunity to speak one week about prayer, where I could share new insights I had gained. This helped to clarify my thoughts and made them even more practical.

// I would like to thank the participants of the camp meeting (*Kurzbibelschule*) at Bogenhofen in 2011. Your encouraging feedback on the topic of prayer motivated me to finish this book even sooner.

// Thank you very much to all faithful prayer partners who have surrounded me with their prayers and have lifted me up into God's presence during many weeks, months, and years. But especially I would like to thank my praying parents, Kurt and Berbel Hasel, whose prayers have carried me from early days on. You are truly faithful praying parents and a great inspiration. Dad, many valuable thoughts in this book were initiated by you. Thank you!

// Without the generous financial help of many donors and friends the realization of this book would not have been possible. Even though your names do not appear here, you know who is meant and how grateful I am for your generosity.

// Thank you, Simone Riedel and your whole family. Because of your faithful weekly cooking ministry you helped me to gain precious time to write so the book could be published earlier. Your meals were a tasty feast in the truest sense of the word.

// My great gratitude belongs to my sons: Jonathan, Florian, and Daniel. I could sense your loyalty and silent support all the way through. And this was very encouraging to me. Daniel, thank you for your grace, your charitable spirit, your patience, and your willingness to spend less time with your dad than I would have loved to spend with you. Perhaps you know better than any other person how much I am still learning those practical lessons of what it means to be a genuine Christian. United with God we will make it. Let's stick to it!

// Thank you to the leadership of Bogenhofen Seminary who supported this project in a very positive way at every stage. The initial idea of it started during a spiritual retreat weekend with the members of the Administrative Committee at Bogenhofen Seminary in September 2010. It is truly amazing to see what God is able to do, even with very humble beginnings. It has been a pleasure to work at a school for some eighteen years where the Bible and prayer are greatly appreciated and have a prominent place in the daily affairs of school life.

// I would like to thank Sigrun Schumacher and Luise Schneeweiß for their editorial skills and their unselfish help.

// Thank you, Markus Kutzschbach, for your inspiration to make the content of this book available to a larger audience.

// I would also like to thank Cindy Tutsch, former associate director at the Ellen G. White Estate, and Janet Page from the Ministerial Association at the General Conference of Seventh-day Adventists for their active interest in the book and their encouragement to translate it into English.

// Without the help of Susi Mundy, my aunt, who did the groundwork of translating the book into English, it would have taken much longer to make it available to the English-speaking world. Thank you, Susi, for all your selfless and good work!

// And thank you, Nancy Wilson, for your enthusiastic support and initiative to get the book finally published in English.

// A heartfelt thank-you also to Jerry Thomas and Scott Cady from Pacific Press, who opened the door to get this book published there, and to all the other competent and efficient workers at Pacific Press who helped to get the process of publishing it in English going and for making it a success.

// But the biggest THANK-YOU belongs to my faithful God and Father in heaven: YOU have not let me down in difficult times and very trying circumstances. YOU cheered me on and helped me when nothing seemed to move forward. I marvel at YOUR patience with me and how YOU succeed in transforming very short periods of time into exceedingly productive time slots where writing and work flower and flourish. More than anything else it is my hope and deep desire that this book will give glory to YOU! May the content of this book help readers to get closer to YOU. May the reading of Your Word and the prayers they speak help them to KNOW YOU BETTER, to TRUST YOU MORE FULLY, and to LOVE YOU MORE DEEPLY.

INTRODUCTION

Taking God at His word is fascinating because the Bible is full of surprises. It describes God in unexpected and unique ways. The encounter with God in the Bible has the power to transform your life. It challenges you in many ways to deepen your thinking and to change your living for the better. It is worthwhile to engage in a study of the Bible. It pays to diligently search the Holy Scriptures. In the living Word of God you find more than interesting information about God. You may encounter God Himself. But in order to discover what the Bible really says, you have to read it for yourself. This book is intended to stimulate such personal Bible study.

THE FIRST PART

The first part offers practical suggestions on how to read the Bible in a profitable way. If you follow the suggested daily reading plan you will read through the whole Bible in the course of one year. Each day you will have the opportunity to read passages from the Old Testament and from the New Testament or the Psalms. If you want to read at a slower pace, you may choose to read only part of the recommended Bible passages. It doesn't matter how much you read every day. To read just a little in the Bible is better than to read nothing at all! In order that thoughts that come to your mind while reading the Bible do not get forgotten, there is space for you to jot them down every day. Looking back, it is often fascinating to see which insights you gained while reading the Bible and which passages of Scripture became valuable to you throughout the year.

The primary goal for reading the Bible is to encounter the living God, not just to expand your knowledge about Him. He is the One who gave us His Word. He reveals Himself in it. In the Holy Scriptures, God has revealed His will and His plan of salvation. In the pages of the Bible, you will meet Jesus Christ, God's Son, who shows you what God is really like. The reading of the Holy Scriptures thus opens new horizons because it leads you to meet the living God, which is truly enriching and life changing.

In every encounter with God and in every reading of the Bible, prayer should play an important role. Hence, there is space every day for you to jot down the personal thoughts of your prayers.

Prayer that pleases God is much more than asking Him to fulfill your wishes. Prayer that pleases God takes you into the immediate presence of God Himself and is an important part of having a vibrant relationship with Him. The purpose of this book is to encourage you in your personal journey with God by stimulating new spiritual life through a meaningful reading of the Bible and by offering you the opportunity to try new ways to enrich your prayer life.

1 The Bible plan will lead you through the whole Bible in one year. Every day you will have the opportunity to read sections from the Old Testament and from the New Testament or the Psalms.

2 Prayer belongs with every encounter with God and the reading of His Word. Therefore, you will find room to write down the thoughts of your prayers each day.

3 Here you will find inspirational thoughts on the Bible and prayer.

4 At the end of each month you will find practical suggestions for prayer to use through the year.

PRAYER JOURNAL

MY PRAISE · MY THANKS · MY PRAYERS

" If from January 1 on you let your Bible gather dust, your soul will have gathered dust by December 31.

Johann Heinrich Michaers
"

January 1

January 2

January 3

22

BIBLE JOURNAL

GOD'S PROMISES · MY KNOWLEDGE

OT *Genesis 1–2* — January 1 — *Matthew 1* NT

OT *Genesis 3–4* — January 2 — *Matthew 2* NT

OT *Genesis 5–6* — January 3 — *Matthew 3* NT

23

---

31 REASONS TO PRAY FOR OTHERS

〜 31 REASONS 〜

1. **Love.** "Lord, let _____ lead a life that is touched by Your love so that all areas of his/her life are directed by Your Holy Spirit who lives in him/her." (Ephesians 5:2; Galatians 5:25)

2. **Yearning for God.** "O Lord, as a deer longs for a stream of cool water, so let _____ long for You, the living God. Satisfy his/her yearning, and give him/her Your peace, which is far beyond human understanding." (Psalm 42:1, 2; Philippians 4:7)

3. **Love for God's Word.** "God, You are the God who speaks, who has created the world through Your powerful word and who has given us the written Word of God, the Bible. Please awake in _____ a love for Your Word so that it will come alive for him/her and become more desirable than fine gold." (Psalm 119:96–98; 19:10)

4. **Uprightness and Truthfulness.** "Dear God, let uprightness and truthfulness grow in the life of _____ because You are a God of truth, and you let the upright succeed." (1 Chronicles 29:17; Proverbs 2:7)

5. **Growing in Grace and Knowledge.** "Gracious Father in heaven, I ask that _____ will grow in the grace and knowledge of our Lord and Savior Jesus Christ and experience Your transforming grace today." (2 Peter 3:18)

6. **Self-Control.** "Good Lord, give _____ the gift of self-control and restraint so that he/she will not damage himself/herself through hasty and thoughtless actions. Let _____ be alert and self-disciplined in everything he/she does." (Proverbs 25:28; James 3:5; 1 Thessalonians 5:6; 2 Timothy 1:7)

7. **Righteousness.** "Righteous God, help _____ to love righteousness in the same way as You are righteous in all You do. Give _____ wisdom and skill to be just in his/her relationships with others." (Psalm 11:7; Micah 6:8)

8. **Mercy.** "Gracious and merciful Father in heaven, let _____ become a merciful person just as You are merciful." (Luke 6:36)

9. **Honor and Respect.** "Heavenly Father, give _____ a proper measure of honor and respect for others because You have created all of us in Your image." (1 Peter 2:17; Romans 12:10; 13:7)

10. **Biblical Self-Esteem.** "Creator God, help that _____ finds his/her value and dignity in the fact that You

150

---

31 REASONS TO PRAY FOR OTHERS

created him/her and have re-created him/her in Jesus Christ for a life of good deeds." (Ephesians 2:10)

11. **Faithfulness.** "Faithful God, let Your faithfulness and loyalty be engraved on the heart of _____ so that he/she will never lose it and will himself/herself be inspired to be a faithful person." (Proverbs 3:3)

12. **Courage.** "Powerful God, let _____ always be strong and courageous in those things that he/she in faith does for You." (Deuteronomy 31:6; Joshua 1:9)

13. **Purity.** "God, create a pure heart in _____ and put a new and loyal spirit in him/her so that his/her pure motives will be apparent in his/her deeds." (Psalm 51:10; Galatians 2:20)

14. **Kindness.** "Our kind Savior and Father in heaven, fill _____ with kindness so that he/she will resemble You in his/her relationships with others." (Galatians 5:22; Colossians 3:12; Titus 3:4)

15. **Gladness.** "God of joy and gladness, fill _____ with joy so that he/she will practice his/her faith with gladness." (Psalm 40:16; Ecclesiastes 3:12)

16. **Helpfulness.** "God, our helper in need, give _____ the willingness to joyfully serve others in their needs and to do good with the means You have given him/her." (1 Timothy 6:18)

17. **Generosity.** "Our Father in heaven, You are a generous God who gladly gives us more than we need. Teach _____ the joy of giving and don't let him/her be penny-pinching, because You love a cheerful giver." (2 Corinthians 9:7, 8)

18. **Peace-Loving.** "Prince of Peace, give _____ the wisdom and the ability to work for peace. Let him/her do everything possible to promote peace. Fill him/her with Your shalom/peace, which is far beyond human understanding." (Matthew 5:9; Philippians 4:7; Romans 14:17)

19. **Joy.** "Father in heaven, let _____ radiate with joy in his/her faith, and fill him/her with Your joy." (Psalm 34:5; Romans 15:13; 1 John 1:4)

20. **Perseverance.** "God of Abraham, Isaac, and Jacob, give _____ perseverance in the tasks You have given him/her to do. Don't let him/her get weary along the way. And give him/her clear goals. Because only those who have a worthwhile goal before their eyes will develop the perseverance to reach it." (Hebrews 12:1; Galatians 6:9)

21. **Faith.** "I pray, Father in heaven, that faith will develop deeper roots in the heart of _____ and that his/her dependence on You and Your Word will grow stronger so that he/she will receive what You have promised those who believe." (Luke 8:5–8, 11–15; Hebrews 11:1)

151

⌒ AT THE END OF EACH MONTH ⌒

At the end of each month you will find further practical tips to help you pray and reflect upon your spiritual life. You will find suggestions on how to pray in such a way that it is pleasing to the heart of God. It will help you to be more focused in your prayers for others. You will learn to reflect upon the nature of God in new ways and experience God differently by way of conscious praise and thanksgiving. You will find encouragement in dealing with difficult and challenging aspects of prayer, such as *What happens when my prayers are not granted? What does it mean to pray and fast? Or How do I get rid of grudges and bitterness?*

⌒ AT THE END OF THE BOOK ⌒

At the end of the book there are suggestions for special prayer emphasis for each day of the week. They can help to provide meaningful structure to your daily prayers. In that way you can, in addition to praise and thanksgiving, take focused prayer requests to God.

This journal offers you the opportunity daily to record your insights while reading God's Word and to jot down your prayers. Thus this book will be a daily companion in your spiritual journey with God. Especially in a time of digital fast pace and shortcuts, to actually write down your thoughts on paper carries a power and beauty of its own that is unsurpassed. To record your experiences with God on paper, to write down insights you have gained, to prevent them from being soon forgotten, a book like this is matchless. You will discover that for yourself, if you will give it a try.

Too quickly do we forget God's blessings and the positive experiences we have had with Him, and then we are often surprised to find ourselves unable to tell others about Him. God knew about our human problem of forgetfulness. It is not without reason that we are admonished in the Bible not to forget His kind acts: "Praise the Lord, my soul, and do not forget how kind he is" (Psalm 103:2, GNT).

One way to counteract our spiritual forgetfulness is to keep a prayer and Bible journal. What distinguishes this prayer and Bible journal from others is the conscious emphasis on God and His Word as the basis of our relationship with Him. Only secondarily is it about our own personal prayer requests. The emphasis on the Word of God will help you to be focused on God even in your personal prayer. Only within the framework of our personal friendship with God will the different daily and weekly prayer suggestions, provided in this book, gain their true meaning and momentum.

The recommendations you find in these pages are meant to stimulate your thinking. They are suggestions rather than requirements. They are intended to invigorate your walk with God and to provide spiritual stimuli that will inspire you to try out ideas for yourself. Here you will not find a secret recipe that will solve all your problems. This book is not about any rituals that are to be performed mechanically. Rather, your own Bible study and your prayer life shall be invigorated and receive new inspiration. You are welcome to try out new things for yourself.

Since the death of my wife in 2009, I have tested all the suggestions of this journal. My spiritual life has been enriched in numerous ways. In hard and difficult times it helped me not to forget God's loving care. When discouraging thoughts burdened my heart, I learned to consciously give thanks. This helped me to be grateful and cheerful again. I learned to express my admiration of the many facets of God's character and His attributes in new and meaningful ways. My appreciation of God's fascinating grace grew deeper. New spiritual impulses invigorated my relationships with my children, my family, my church, my neighbors, and the people surrounding the area in which I live and work.

This journal will help you not to forget the manifold blessings of God. It will help you to understand Him even better and to love Him more deeply. Possibly the most surprising side effect, however, is the positive change your life undergoes through the encounter with God's Word. To be connected through prayer with the living God of the Bible affects your life as nothing else ever can. Eventually, it contributes to becoming more like Jesus. That is my wish for your life.

PRODUCTIVE BIBLE STUDY

Nothing strengthens the mind more than Bible study. No other book has such power to uplift our thoughts and to change us for the good. The Bible shows us how we really are. It brings us close to God and reveals to us what is important to Him. It can be understood by simple people—even by children—yet it offers the best-educated people opportunities to learn new things. Reading the Bible literally opens up new dimensions and imparts unique values. To maximize these possibilities, observe the following suggestions.

OPENNESS AND READINESS TO LEARN

As much as possible, lay aside all prejudices and preconceived ideas when you read the Bible. Those who read the Bible to confirm their own ideas cannot expect to be changed by it and to learn new things. Form your opinions according to the Word of God. Do not shape your reading of the Bible according to your preconceived opinions. God knows your inward attitude. Integrity is pleasing to Him (1 Chronicles 29:17). Proverbs 2:7 says, "He provides help and protection for those who are righteous and honest" (GNT). Jesus said, "Whoever is willing to do what God wants will know whether what I teach comes from God or whether I speak on my own authority" (John 7:17, GNT).

LOVING OBEDIENCE

The message of the Bible remains locked when we hold on to skepticism. It is not systematic doubt and criticism but an attitude of love and obedience that lets you understand God's Word at a deeper level and that opens the treasures of the Bible to you (see 1 Corinthians 2:9, 10). Love trusts the other person and has the courage to put new knowledge to work in your own life. That is how the door is opened for yet further insight and growth. God can give you this willingness (Philippians 2:13).

∽ PERSEVERANCE ∾

America was not discovered in one day. Similarly, discovering valuable insights may demand perseverance. In Proverbs 2:3–5 you glimpse a sense of this perseverance:

> and if you call out for insight
>   and cry aloud for understanding,
> and if you look for it as for silver
>   and search for it as for hidden treasure,
> then you will understand the fear of the LORD
>   and find the knowledge of God.

It is worthwhile to search for the treasures in the Bible with persistence. Even if at a first reading you don't understand everything, and some things seem strange or difficult, stay with it and continue reading! Put to practice the things you do understand. And take into consideration that each insight takes time to mature. If you skipped your Bible reading for a day (or two or three . . .), start reading again. It is always possible to start reading the Bible. And it is never too late to start reading your Bible!

∽ RESERVE A SPECIFIC TIME AND A QUIET LOCATION ∾

If you are in love, you enjoy spending time alone with the loved one. Choose a place in which you can read and reflect on God's Word without interruptions. In our hectic life this can succeed only if you deliberately keep a specific window of time open. Often the first hours of the day are best for those minutes of quietness and contemplation. Those precious moments, before your work starts, can become a blessing for the rest of the day because the first thoughts often accompany you for many hours. Perhaps some other quiet time during the day will work better for you when you can spend some minutes with God and His Word without interruption. Be creative. And if in the evening, before going to bed, you let the day end with a few thoughts from the Bible, then you might share the experience of the psalmist who finds "delight" in God's Word, "and in His law he meditates day and night" (Psalm 1:2, NASB).

ᘓ PRAYER ᘓ

No one can grant better insights into the Bible than the One who inspired the Holy Scriptures (see 2 Timothy 3:16; 2 Peter 1:19–21). The Holy Spirit not only will help you understand spiritual things from God's perspective but also will stir in you the desire to be obedient to the Word of God. With your prayer you express your desire for God's guidance and your readiness to be obedient. Remember that the Holy Spirit will always guide you in accordance and in harmony with the Word of God. He will not negate clear statements of the Bible but will lead you to willing obedience in agreement with the Word of God. And, by the way, when you are on your knees, you will truly gain a new perspective on many problems of life.

ᘓ READING WITH OPEN EYES ᘓ

Only when you actually read the Bible will you get to know the Bible and understand it. Personally becoming acquainted with the Bible is better than hearing something *about* the Bible. While you read the Bible, you become immersed in its train of thought, and you begin to think and reason along those lines. Read even the well-known passages in the Bible with open eyes. Ask yourself questions like the following: *What do I notice? What exactly is the text saying? Which concepts appear repeatedly? Who is mentioned? How does something happen? What does it lead to? When will it happen? What am I learning about God? What am I learning about myself? How is God described? Why is this important to God? Which characteristics of God are mentioned? How have people experienced God/Jesus?* Then write the thoughts down in your prayer and Bible journal.

Only a book that has been underlined and marked is a book that has truly been read. When you underline statements in the Bible, it is easier to find them again. The following colors and symbols can be of help:

Red = Positive things, God's promises
Yellow = Holy Spirit, Inspiration
Green = Second coming of Jesus
Blue = Faith, baptism, church

Purple = Sanctuary
Brown = Prophecies
Black = Sin
Etc.

Symbol	Meaning	Symbol	Meaning
☁	Coming of Jesus	☺	Joy
☀	Resurrection	Ψ	Satan
J	References to Jesus	∅	Warning
⫸	Promises	→J	Discipleship, following Jesus
✸	God's guidance/leading	M	Mission
®	God's Word	⚒	Judgment
✿	Growth in faith, sanctification	\○/	Encouraging words
☾✶	Creation	RIP	State of the dead
⋒	God's law, obedience	☌	Holy Spirit
7	Sabbath	♡	Loving your neighbor
✝	Salvation	A⁺	Education
∪	Conversion, repentance	☹	Sin
P	Prayer	◗	Baptism
♫	Praise and thanks	$	Tithe and offerings
⌂	Church	⊂⊃	Divinity of Jesus

∾ APPLICATION ∾

If you implement and follow what you have read and understood, you will gain a deeper understanding of biblical truth. Insight grows through obedience. The following questions can be helpful to ponder: *What does that mean for my life? What consequences do I draw for my life? What should I change? How can I apply what I have read and learned in my own life? How can I share with others what I have learned? What is of importance to me?* Write your insights down in your prayer and Bible journal. Only the person who reads the Bible can profit from God's Word. Reserve some special time—day by day—and give it a try. It is worth the effort.

LONGING FOR GOD

························

PRAYER JOURNAL
&
BIBLE JOURNAL

JANUARY

"

If from January 1
on you let your
Bible gather dust,
your soul will have
gathered dust by
December 31.

Johann Hinrich Wichern

"

January 1

January 2

January 3

OT *Genesis 1; 2*   January 1   *Matthew 1* NT

OT *Genesis 3; 4*   January 2   *Matthew 2* NT

OT *Genesis 5; 6*   January 3   *Matthew 3* NT

JAN

"

Every day should begin with reading the Bible and with prayer. Sin will keep you from this Book, or this Book will keep you from sin.

....

John Bunyan

"

January 4

January 5

January 6

OT *Genesis 7; 8*   # January 4   *Psalms 1; 2*   Ps

OT *Genesis 9–11*   # January 5   *Matthew 4* NT

OT *Genesis 12; 13*   # January 6   *Matthew 5* NT

JAN

JAN

The study of the Scriptures is the means divinely ordained to bring men into closer connection with their Creator and to give them a clearer knowledge of His will. It is the medium of communication between God and man.

....

Ellen G. White, *The Great Controversy Between Christ and Satan*, p. 69

January 7

January 8

January 9

OT *Genesis 14; 15* January 7 *Psalms 3; 4* Ps

OT *Genesis 16; 17* January 8 *Matthew 6* NT

OT *Genesis 18; 19* January 9 *Matthew 7* NT

JAN

66

The person who begins to read the Bible will ask the usual questions, impatient, uncom-prehending, haughty questions. All these questions find no answer. He who continues to read in spite of that he discovers that the Bible begins to ask him questions. The one who does not avoid them finds the gate to life.

....

Horst Bannach

99

January 10

January 11

January 12

OT *Genesis 20; 21* January 10 *Matthew 8* NT

OT *Genesis 22; 23* January 11 *Psalms 5; 6* Ps

OT *Genesis 24; 25* January 12 *Matthew 9* NT

66

Through prayer
dust disappears
from the soul, and
burdens from the
conscience, and fear
from the heart.

....

Hermann von Bezzel

99

January 13

January 14

January 15

OT *Genesis 26; 27*   January 13   *Matthew 10* NT

_____
_____
_____
_____
_____
_____

OT *Genesis 28; 29*   January 14   *Psalms 7; 8* Ps

_____
_____
_____
_____
_____
_____

OT *Genesis 30; 31*   January 15   *Matthew 11* NT

_____
_____
_____
_____
_____
_____

JAN

66

The Bible gives
us directions for
living our life.
He who reads the
Bible stands on
solid ground. On
the foundation of
facts and on a base
that holds one up,
especially in crises.

....

Peter Hahne

99

January 16

January 17

January 18

OT *Genesis 32; 33*   January 16   *Matthew 12* NT

_____

_____

_____

_____

_____

_____

_____

OT *Genesis 34–36*   January 17   *Matthew 13* NT

_____

_____

_____

_____

_____

_____

_____

OT *Genesis 37; 38*   January 18   *Psalm 9* Ps

_____

_____

_____

_____

_____

_____

_____

JAN

66

Prayer is the door
that leads us out
of the prison of
our worries.

....

Helmut Gollwitzer

99

January 19

January 20

January 21

OT *Genesis 39; 40*

January 19

Matthew 14 NT

OT *Genesis 41; 42*

January 20

Matthew 15 NT

OT *Genesis 43; 44*

January 21

Psalm 10 Ps

JAN

"

The Bible does not exist so that we can criticize it but rather so that it can criticize us.

....

Søren Kierkegaard

"

January 22

January 23

January 24

OT *Genesis 45; 46*　　　January 22　　　*Matthew 16* NT

OT *Genesis 47; 48*　　　January 23　　　*Matthew 17* NT

OT *Genesis 49; 50*　　　January 24　　　*Matthew 18* NT

JAN

66

We hear it said that "Prayer alters things"; prayer not so much alters things as alters the man who prays.

Oswald Chambers

99

January 25

January 26

January 27

OT *Exodus 1; 2*   # January 25   *Psalms 11; 12* Ps

OT *Exodus 3; 4*   # January 26   *Matthew 19* NT

OT *Exodus 5; 6*   # January 27   *Matthew 20* NT

JAN

66

There are talented painters who can capture an entire landscape with a few strokes of the brush. I believe that the Holy Scriptures are a master in this art. The Bible only says a few words; but it seems to me that it has understood all of us and our condition in one sweep.

Johannes Busch

99

January 28

January 29

January 30

January 31

GOD'S PROMISES - MY KNOWLEDGE

OT *Exodus 7; 8*   January 28   *Psalms 13; 14* Ps

OT *Exodus 9; 10*   January 29   *Matthew 21* NT

OT *Exodus 11; 12*   January 30   *Matthew 22* NT

OT *Exodus 13; 14*   January 31   *Matthew 23* NT

MORE THOUGHTS

PRAYER
That Pleases God

JANUARY

*Practical suggestions for prayer and proven suggestions
to think about your faith life*

✃ MANY PRAYERS COME FROM WRONG MOTIVES ✃

Many prayers, even though disguised in a pious cloak, are in the final analysis based on wrong motives. I might pray for another person because I am afraid of losing a precious friendship. I might pray for success in the cause of God because I am playing an important role in it and my influence will be strengthened if what I pray for succeeds. I might ask to be spared a defeat because I am ashamed of failure and do not want to face the malicious comments of others. I might pray for health because I am afraid of pain and do not want to live a restricted or handicapped life. I might pray that someone's life be spared because I do not like living alone. I might pray for the conversion of a person because my life will then be easier. I might pray to find a significant other because I yearn for love and seek recognition. I might ask God for specific things because I have become used to a certain standard of living and am not content with less. I might ask for success because I desire money and wealth and the admiration of others. And if I do not get what I am asking for right away, I intensify my prayer and pray even harder. But actually, my prayers often center only around myself. They speak about what *I* wish to have. What *I* want to receive from God. Sometimes even in His name.

✃ PRAYER THAT IS PLEASING TO GOD ✃
HAS GOD AT ITS CENTER

Prayer that is pleasing to God has a refreshingly different focus. No longer is my "want-to-have" the center of my prayer. Instead, God becomes central. That is the crucial and all-important point. First of all, prayer that is pleasing to God recognizes God as a faithful friend whose companionship I seek because *He* is important to me, not because I want something from Him. God's presence is much more important than the things He gives to me. In His presence, I feel sheltered. Without Him I don't want to live. That is the reason why I want to get to know Him better. I want to learn from Him. Without Him my life would lack the decisive perspective. More important than anything I can ask for is my desire to be with Him. The time I spend with Him is precious—because He is precious to me. I can confide everything to Him. He understands me. He loves me tenderly. He wants to be with me. I long to be with Him. That is the center of true prayer.[1]

Prayer that is pleasing to God is focused on God. It begins with a personal communion with Him, not with my wishes and requests. It is not about following specific religious formulas or adhering to specific prayer techniques that are supposed to guarantee the fulfillment of my wishes. Prayer that pleases God has Him at the center and relates to Him. When my request, even my intercessory prayer, is not anchored in this living relationship with Him, it relates more to my wishes and my well-being than to God and His will. Without this living friendship with God, my prayer resembles more the operation of a divine prayer machine: I feed in my prayer requests at the top and take out my granted wishes at the bottom.

IT IS NOT A MATTER OF FOLLOWING SPECIFIC PRAYER TECHNIQUES

First, prayer that pleases God enjoys spending time in the presence of God and expresses my admiration and love for Him. Once I understand that my relationship with God is the center of my prayer, my prayer requests gain a totally new focus. I begin to think and pray from God's perspective. I start to view my requests, my wishes, my yearnings, my whole life through His eyes. I tell Him what is really on my heart, what makes me insecure, what makes me anxious, for what I really yearn deep inside, what I desire, what I would rather avoid, what embarrasses me, what gives me pleasure, what makes me shout with joy, and what drives me to despair. In short, I share my life with God. If we remove the relationship aspect from prayer, prayer becomes one-sided, selfish, and wrong.

God is deeply interested in me. He longs to be part of me, in all aspects of my life: my worries, my fears, my wishes, my hopes, my wants, my abilities, my yearnings, my success, my honor, my recognition, my joy, my children, my money, my possessions, my friendship, my marriage, my needs, my health, my talents, my plans, my love, my anger, my creativity, my energy, my thoughts, my admiration, my music, my praise, my gratitude, my appearance—in short, my entire life. I talk about these things with Him as with a good friend. And I look at all of it through His eyes.

❧ PRAYER THAT PLEASES GOD ❧
IS BASED ON RELATIONSHIP

Prayer that pleases God frees my thinking from revolving around the "I." It allows me to become honest with myself and with God. In the light of His love and His holiness, I begin to see myself differently. Gently I move toward the true purpose of prayer: not the fulfillment of my wishes but the relationship with the life-changing God. To pray in this way fills my life with the knowledge that He is the center of my life. My thoughts and wishes are in accordance with Him. To pray in this way is a real challenge. It is only too easy to pray as I would normally do. It is so easy to ask God for something before I have enjoyed His companionship. In more than a thousand ways I am told that God will give me that for which I ask Him, and my natural, sinful heart insists that all my wishes be fulfilled. Often the fulfillment of my wishes is more important than my relationship with Him.

However, prayer that pleases God has God at its center. It opens up new perspectives. When I consciously think about His character, His qualities and abilities, and express my adoration for them in my own words, my prayers are filled with spiritual life and even have an element of reverence and admiration that goes along with them. No longer are my problems and needs the center of my prayers, but God is the center. Prayer that pleases God means to step into His presence. It is an expression of my relationship with Him. Prayer does not bring God down to me; it lifts me up into His presence. Prayer does not change God; it changes me. Start to pray like that. It will change your life. Try it out!

"You need not go to the ends of the earth for wisdom, for God is near. It is not the capabilities you now possess or ever will have that will give you success. It is that which the Lord can do for you. We need to have far less confidence in what man can do and far more confidence in what God can do for every believing soul. He longs to have you reach after Him by faith. He longs to have you expect great things from Him. He longs to give you understanding in temporal as well as in spiritual matters. He can sharpen the intellect. He can give tact and skill. Put your talents into the work, ask God for wisdom, and it will be given you."[2]

---

1. I have taken the above suggestions from a book by Larry Crabb that is well worth reading, *The Papa Prayer: The Prayer You've Never Prayed* (Nashville, TN: Thomas Nelson, 2006). The book contains many additional helpful thoughts.

2. Ellen G. White, *Christ's Object Lessons*, 146.

LONGING FOR GOD

PRAYER JOURNAL
&
BIBLE JOURNAL

FEBRUARY

FEB

"

We do not pray in order to let God know what we want because He knows our heart better than we do ourselves; rather, he who prays lives before Him, toward Him, from Him, gives God what belongs to Him and receives what He wants to give.

....

Romano Guardini

"

February 1

February 2

February 3

OT *Exodus 15; 16* | February 1 | *Psalms 15; 16* Ps

_____
_____
_____
_____
_____
_____
_____

OT *Exodus 17; 18* | February 2 | *Matthew 24* NT

_____
_____
_____
_____
_____
_____
_____

OT *Exodus 19; 20* | February 3 | *Matthew 25* NT

_____
_____
_____
_____
_____
_____
_____

66

In this the Bible
resembles the night
sky: the longer you
look, the more stars
there are!

. . . .

Dmitri Sergejewitsch
Mereschkowski

99

FEB

February 4

February 5

February 6

OT *Exodus 21; 22* February 4 *Psalm 17* Ps

FEB

OT *Exodus 23; 24* February 5 *Matthew 26* NT

OT *Exodus 25; 26* February 6 *Matthew 27* NT

FEB

"

Prayer, in the sense of petition, asking for things, is a small part of it; confession and penitence are its threshold, adoration its sanctuary, the presence and vision and enjoyment of God its bread and wine.

C. S. Lewis

"

February 7

February 8

February 9

OT *Exodus 27; 28*   February 7   *Psalm 18* Ps

OT *Exodus 29; 30*   February 8   *Matthew 28* NT

OT *Exodus 31; 32*   February 9   *Acts 1* NT

66

As one reads the Bible, so will be the direction of his house. In the Bible you find not simply words to read, but words to live by.

....
Martin Luther

99

February 10

February 11

February 12

OT *Exodus 33; 34*   **February 10**   *Acts 2* NT

OT *Exodus 35; 36*   **February 11**   *Psalm 19* Ps

OT *Exodus 37; 38*   **February 12**   *Acts 3* NT

FEB

February 13

"

Talking with God is incomparably more important than talking about God.

....

Hans Asmussen

"

February 14

February 15

OT *Exodus 39; 40*   February 13   *Acts 4* NT

OT *Leviticus 1–3*   February 14   *Acts 5* NT

OT *Leviticus 4; 5*   February 15   *Psalms 20; 21* Ps

MY PRAISE · MY THANKS · MY PRAYERS

FEB

"

The Bible was not written for the scholar alone; on the contrary, it was designed for the common people. The great truths necessary for salvation are made as clear as noonday; and none will mistake and lose their way except those who follow their own judgment instead of the plainly revealed will of God.

....

Ellen G. White,
Steps to Christ, p. 89

"

February 16

February 17

February 18

OT *Leviticus 6; 7*   February 16   *Acts 6* NT

FEB

OT *Leviticus 8; 9*   February 17   *Acts 7* NT

OT *Leviticus 10–12*   February 18   *Psalm 22* Ps

FEB

66

Here is the problem: not if our prayers find fulfillment but rather if we can find people who pray.

....

Helmut Thielicke

99

February 19

February 20

February 21

OT *Leviticus 13; 14*   February 19   *Acts 8* NT

OT *Leviticus 15; 16*   February 20   *Acts 9* NT

OT *Leviticus 17; 18*   February 21   *Acts 10* NT

FEB

66

The difficulties of Scripture have been urged by skeptics as an argument against the Bible; but so far from this, they constitute a strong evidence of its divine inspiration. If it contained no account of God but that which we could easily comprehend; if His greatness and majesty could be grasped by finite minds, then the Bible would not bear the unmistakable credentials of divine authority. The very grandeur and mystery of the themes presented should inspire faith in it as the word of God.

Ellen G. White, *Testimonies for the Church*, vol. 5, p. 700

99

February 22

February 23

February 24

OT *Leviticus 19; 20*   **February 22**   *Psalms 23; 24* Ps

OT *Leviticus 21; 22*   **February 23**   *Acts 11* NT

OT *Leviticus 23; 24*   **February 24**   *Acts 12* NT

FEB

"

Out of the prayer of repentance arises the song of praise.

....

Jochen Klepper

"

February 25

February 26

February 27

OT *Leviticus 25; 26*   February 25   *Psalm 25* Ps

OT *Leviticus 27; Numbers 1*   February 26   *Acts 13* NT

OT *Numbers 2; 3*   February 27   *Acts 14* NT

MY PRAISE · MY THANKS · MY PRAYERS

FEB

66

The Bible is a window in this prison-world, through which we may look into eternity.

....

Timothy Dwight

99

February 28

[February 29]

OT *Numbers 4; 5*   **February 28**   *Acts 15* NT

[February 29]

MORE THOUGHTS

························

THANKING
GOD

FEBRUARY

*Practical suggestions for prayer and proven suggestions
to think about your faith life*

In everything give thanks; for this is God's will for you in Christ Jesus.
—1 Thessalonians 5:18 (NASB)

Being thankful changes our life for the better. Giving thanks brings countless blessings. Giving thanks is God's way for our life. The one who exercises a thankful spirit lives not just more gratefully but also more happily and thereby in the end also more healthfully. Giving thanks means to remember that someone has done something good for me, and I express my appreciation in words. Gratitude changes my perspective and opens up a positive attitude toward life.

You can noticeably experience the life-changing effects of thankfulness if you practice the following simple exercise for several days: Every day write down ten different words that summarize things for which you are grateful. You can start by writing down ten things in the list below. After you have written down ten words (e.g., eyes, bed, house, etc.), think about what these things mean to you (e.g., What do my eyes mean to me? What do my eyes make possible? What would I not be able to do if I were blind? What does my bed mean to me? How would it be if I always had to sleep on a hard and cold floor? What does my home mean to me? What would it be like if I did not have the privacy of my own home? etc.). Then take each word and write a short sentence expressing your gratitude to Jesus (e.g., "Lord Jesus, thank You for my eyes with which I can see colors and read books." "Lord Jesus, thank You for my bed . . .," etc.). Say each of these sentences out loud so you can hear your own voice. The next day, write ten more things for which you are grateful and repeat the whole process. If you want to intensify this process, also repeat the items from the previous day. At the end of just one week, you will already have seventy (!) reasons to be grateful. In one month's time, at the most, gratitude will have changed your life. Guaranteed!

FEB

Reasons to Be Thankful:

Thank-You Note:

Reasons to Be Thankful:

Thank-You Note:

LONGING FOR GOD

PRAYER JOURNAL
&
BIBLE JOURNAL

MARCH

> **"**
>
> We dare not minimize the fact that Jesus sought time in solitude with the heavenly Father before every important decision and action during His public ministry.
>
> ....
>
> Gordon MacDonald
>
> **"**

March 1

March 2

March 3

....

GOD'S PROMISES - MY KNOWLEDGE

OT *Numbers 6; 7*   March 1   *Psalms 26; 27* Ps

_____
_____
_____
_____
_____
_____

OT *Numbers 8; 9*   March 2   *Acts 16* NT

_____
_____
_____
_____
_____
_____

OT *Numbers 10; 11*   March 3   *Acts 17* NT

_____
_____
_____
_____
_____
_____

MAR

MAR

"

An honest man
with an open
Bible and a pad
and pencil is sure
to find out what
is wrong with him
very quickly.

....

A. W. Tozer

"

March 4

March 5

March 6

OT *Numbers 12–14*　　　　　# March 4　　　　　*Psalms 28; 29*　Ps

MAR

OT *Numbers 15; 16*　　　　　# March 5　　　　　*Acts 18* NT

OT *Numbers 17–19*　　　　　# March 6　　　　　*Acts 19* NT

66

Short prayers are
long enough.

....

C. H. Spurgeon

99

MAR

March 7

March 8

March 9

OT *Numbers 20; 21*   March 7   *Acts 20* NT

OT *Numbers 22; 23*   March 8   *Psalm 30* Ps

OT *Numbers 24; 25*   March 9   *Acts 21* NT

MAR

66

Readers of the Bible are leaders because they know in which direction to go.

....

Peter Hahne

99

MAR

March 10

March 11

March 12

OT *Numbers 26; 27*   March 10   *Acts 22* NT

MAR

OT *Numbers 28; 29*   March 11   *Psalm 31*   Ps

OT *Numbers 30; 31*   March 12   *Acts 23* NT

MY PRAISE · MY THANKS · MY PRAYERS

66

Prayer is a resting
place for each grief.

....

J. Chrysostomus

99

MAR

March 13

March 14

March 15

OT *Numbers 32; 33*   March 13   *Acts 24* NT

MAR

OT *Numbers 34; 35*   March 14   *Acts 25* NT

OT *Numbers 36; Deuteronomy 1*   March 15   *Psalm 32* Ps

66

The inconsistencies of Christian people, who while professing to believe their Bibles were yet content to live just as they would if there were no such book, had been one of the strongest arguments of my skeptical companions.

Hudson Taylor

99

March 16

March 17

March 18

OT *Deuteronomy 2; 3*   March 16   *Acts 26* NT

OT *Deuteronomy 4; 5*   March 17   *Acts 27* NT

OT *Deuteronomy 6; 7*   March 18   *Psalm 33* Ps

MAR

66

Courage is fear that
has said its prayers.

....
Karle Wilson Baker

99

MAR

March 19

March 20

March 21

OT *Deuteronomy 8; 9*   # March 19   *Acts 28* NT

_____

_____

_____

_____

_____

_____

_____

_____

MAR

OT *Deuteronomy 10; 11*   # March 20   *Romans 1* NT

_____

_____

_____

_____

_____

_____

_____

_____

OT *Deuteronomy 12–14*   # March 21   *Romans 2* NT

_____

_____

_____

_____

_____

_____

_____

66

Nobody ever
outgrows
Scripture; the
Book widens and
deepens with our
years.

....

C. H. Spurgeon

99

MAR

March 22

March 23

March 24

OT *Deuteronomy 15; 16*   March 22   *Psalm 34* Ps

OT *Deuteronomy 17; 18*   March 23   *Romans 3* NT

OT *Deuteronomy 19; 20*   March 24   *Romans 4* NT

MAR

66

The power of prayer cannot even be demonstrated by Newton.

·········

Stefan Bucholz

99

MAR

March 25

March 26

March 27

OT *Deuteronomy 21; 22*   # March 25   *Psalm 35*   Ps

OT *Deuteronomy 23; 24*   # March 26   *Romans 5* NT

OT *Deuteronomy 25; 26*   # March 27   *Romans 6* NT

MAR

MAR

66

There are people who don't need the Bible. I don't belong to them. . . . I need it in order to understand where I came from. . . . I need it in order to know that someone is above me and has something to say to me. I need it because I have noticed that in decisive moments we humans are not able to comfort each other and that even my own heart finds comfort only there.

....

Jörg Zink

99

March 28

March 29

March 30

March 31

OT *Deuteronomy 27; 28*   March 28   *Romans 7* NT

_____

_____

_____

_____

MAR

OT *Deuteronomy 29; 30*   March 29   *Psalm 36* Ps

_____

_____

_____

_____

OT *Deuteronomy 31; 32*   March 30   *Romans 8* NT

_____

_____

_____

_____

OT *Deuteronomy 33; 34*   March 31   *Romans 9* NT

_____

_____

_____

_____

MORE THOUGHTS

PRAISING
GOD

MARCH

✕

*Practical suggestions for prayer and proven suggestions
to think about your faith life*

Enter His gates with thanksgiving
And His courts with praise.
Give thanks to Him, bless His name. —Psalm 100:4 (NASB)

Praise the LORD.

Praise the LORD, O my soul.
 I will praise the LORD all my life;
 I will sing praise to my God as long as I live. —Psalm 146:1, 2

In the Bible we constantly meet people who praise God. We notice, however, that to praise God means much more than to say the words "I praise the Lord!" I actually praise God when I state my appreciation of His character, His actions, and His ways in positive words. When I praise God, I express my joy, my appreciation, and also my enthusiasm and excitement about God. It is especially worthwhile to contemplate God's nature, His qualities, His character, and His abilities. When I express what I appreciate about God, what certain qualities of God mean to me, why they fill me with joy, and why I do not want to miss them anymore, then I am praising God.

While reading the Bible, if you come across a character trait or a quality of God that fascinates you and that arouses your admiration, write it down. Now consider what this quality means to you. Write down what you appreciate so much about God and why this trait of God is so important and meaningful to you. For example, let's take God's omniscience (see Psalm 139:1–18; 1 John 3:20). I am glad that God knows everything because that means that there will never be a situation for which He is unprepared. God is omniscient; this means He knows everything. This gives me the certainty that God never meets a situation for which He does not know a solution. It calms me to know that God does not overlook anything or forget some important aspect. He even knows what is still in the future. That is why in the Scriptures He acts according to His omniscience by imparting wisdom or revealing hidden things. That truly fascinates me about God. That is something where I can praise Him with all my heart and mind. Only through my conscious contemplation of God's character and His acts am I able to truly praise Him.

This month write down a number of character traits about God that fascinate you, and reflect on what they mean to you. Give praise to God for who He truly is.

Characteristics of God:

What It Means to Me:

Characteristics of God:

What It Means to Me:

LONGING FOR GOD

PRAYER JOURNAL
&
BIBLE JOURNAL

APRIL

66

Funny that when we pray, we often can't think of anything to say; but when we are talking on the telephone, we don't find it hard at all to talk about others.

....

Anonymous

99

APR

April 1

April 2

April 3

OT *Joshua 1–3*   **April 1**   *Psalm 37* Ps

_____
_____
_____
_____
_____
_____
_____
_____
_____

APR

OT *Joshua 4; 5*   **April 2**   *Romans 10* NT

_____
_____
_____
_____
_____
_____
_____
_____
_____

OT *Joshua 6; 7*   **April 3**   *Romans 11* NT

_____
_____
_____
_____
_____
_____
_____
_____

66

My mother gave me the best Bible translation. She translated the Bible into life.

....

John Thiessen

99

April 4

April 5

April 6

OT *Joshua 8; 9*

April 4

Romans 12 NT

OT *Joshua 10; 11*

April 5

Psalm 38 Ps

OT *Joshua 12–15*

April 6

Romans 13 NT

APR

66

I have so much to
do that I spend
several hours in
prayer before I am
able to do it.

. . . .

John Wesley

99

April 7

April 8

April 9

OT *Joshua 16–19*   April 7   *Romans 14* NT

_____
_____
_____
_____
_____
_____
_____

OT *Joshua 20–22*   April 8   *Psalm 39* Ps

_____
_____
_____
_____
_____
_____
_____

OT *Joshua 23; 24*   April 9   *Romans 15* NT

_____
_____
_____
_____
_____
_____
_____

APR

66

It ain't those parts
of the Bible that I
can't understand
that bother me, it is
the parts that I do
understand.

....

Mark Twain

99

APR

April 10

April 11

April 12

OT *Judges 1; 2*　　　　April 10　　　　*Romans 16* NT

OT *Judges 3; 4*　　　　April 11　　　　*Mark 1* NT

OT *Judges 5; 6*　　　　April 12　　　　*Psalms 40; 41* Ps

"

Worries drive me to prayer, and in turn prayer drives worries out.

....

Ulrich Zwingli

"

APR

April 13

April 14

April 15

OT *Judges 7; 8*   April 13   *Mark 2* NT

OT *Judges 9; 10*   April 14   *Mark 3* NT

OT *Judges 11; 12*   April 15   *Psalms 42; 43* Ps

66

The person who does not read his Bible has no advantage over the person who does not possess a Bible.

....

Unknown

99

APR

April 16

April 17

April 18

OT *Judges 13; 14*　　　　　　April 16　　　　　　*Mark 4* NT

OT *Judges 15; 16*　　　　　　April 17　　　　　　*Mark 5* NT

OT *Judges 17; 18*　　　　　　April 18　　　　　　*Mark 6* NT

APR

"

What most often
interrupts my own
prayers is not great
distractions but tiny
ones—things one
will have to do or
avoid in the course
of the next hour.

C. S. Lewis

"

April 19

April 20

April 21

OT *Judges 19; 20* April 19 *Psalm 44* Ps

OT *Judges 21* April 20 *Mark 7* NT

OT *Ruth 1; 2* April 21 *Mark 8* NT

APR

66

The Bible has to change from a book for reading to a book for life.

....

Peter Hahne

99

APR

April 22

April 23

April 24

OT *Ruth 3; 4*   April 22   *Psalm 45* Ps

OT *1 Samuel 1–3*   April 23   *Mark 9* NT

OT *1 Samuel 4–6*   April 24   *Mark 10* NT

APR

"

Any concern too
small to be turned
into a prayer is too
small to be made
into a burden.

....

Corrie ten Boom

"

APR

April 25

April 26

April 27

OT *1 Samuel 7–9*　·　April 25　*Mark 11* NT

OT *1 Samuel 10; 11*　April 26　*Psalms 46; 47* Ps

OT *1 Samuel 12; 13*　April 27　*Mark 12* NT

APR

66

You can read the Bible without understanding it; but you cannot understand it without reading it.

....
Anonymous

99

APR

April 28

April 29

April 30

OT *1 Samuel 14; 15*   April 28   *Mark 13* NT

OT *1 Samuel 16; 17*   April 29   *Psalm 48*   Ps

OT *1 Samuel 18; 19*   April 30   *Mark 14* NT

MORE THOUGHTS

·····················

THE A-B-Cs
of Bible Prayer

APRIL

✕

*Practical suggestions for prayer and proven suggestions
to think about your faith life*

Before you consider the A-B-Cs of prayer,
read the chapter "Prayer That Pleases God."
Only when you pray in the way that pleases God
can you correctly practice the A-B-Cs of prayer.

To use the Bible to pray according to the will of God also means to claim the promises of His Word. By faith you may claim every promise in the Bible for yourself and receive the promised gift from His hands (2 Corinthians 1:20). One way to successfully claim God's promises is the "A-B-Cs of Bible Prayer." It is the key to the biblical prayer according to God's promises. Each letter represents an important principle.[1]

APR

❧ A = ASK ❧

We truly can ask God for anything. No request is too small or unimportant for Him. No request is so big that God cannot handle it. He is omnipotent—and that makes it possible for Him to do VERY much! Jesus Christ says, "Whatever things you ask when you pray, believe that you receive them, and you will have them" (Mark 11:24, NKJV). However, there are certain conditions to observe.

Jesus promises in John 15:7, "If you remain in me and my words remain in you, ask whatever you wish, and it will be given you." If I only ask God for something that *I* want without first being in communion with Him, I abuse prayer and use God only as my divine servant. In this case I don't pray in such a way that pleases God but only in the way that pleases me. Thus, the following Bible verses apply:

This is the confidence we have in approaching God: that if we ask anything according to his will, he hears us. And if we know that he hears us—whatever we ask—we know that we have what we asked of him (1 John 5:14, 15).

If I had cherished sin in my heart, the Lord would not have listened (Psalm 66:18).

If I am not willing to submit my will fully to God because *I* am the center of my life (rather than God being the center), God will hardly answer my prayer (see Isaiah 59:1, 2). An important prerequisite for the fulfillment of my prayers is that I wholeheartedly accept God's will and wholeheartedly reject sin. When my request is fully in harmony with God's will and grows out of my relationship with Him, I may ask for anything that God has promised. And what I then receive from Him should be used to glorify Him.

B = BELIEVE

To pray in the way that pleases God, I must believe. In the Bible, believing is related to trusting. I can only trust someone when I know the person and know that he or she is trustworthy. God has proven in His Son, Jesus Christ, that He is utterly trustworthy and that He keeps His word and fulfills His promises. When I doubt God's goodness and that He will keep His promises, I waver and should not expect that I will receive anything from God (James 1:6–8). To believe means to take God at His word. In faith, I depend on God and His trustworthy promises even if I don't feel anything. Because to have faith means to be "certain of what we do not see" (Hebrews 11:1). "Without faith it is impossible to please God" (v. 6).

C = CLAIM

All my faith is useless if I do not claim the things for which I asked God. I claim the promised gifts of God when I thank Christ for them even before I have received them. John writes, "And if we know that he hears us—whatever we ask—we know that we have what we asked of him" (1 John 5:15). In Luke 8:11 Jesus compares the Word of God to a seed. In the same way that the whole apple tree is contained in an apple seed, the gift of God is contained in His promises. When we claim the promise, we already possess the gift. Let me illustrate: When I receive a check that is covered and signed, at what point does the money belong to me? Immediately when I accept the check! When I cash it, I receive the money for which it was made out. It is the same way with the promises. I receive the promised gift by faith even before I can feel or see it. God will activate the gift, which we already possess by faith, when we have need of it.

The example of the resurrection of Lazarus in John 11 illustrates that Jesus also prayed in this way. We can see that in the following verses:

Verses 3, 4, 23:
Jesus knew exactly what God's will in this situation was.

Verse 11:
He was willing to do God's will; He was always obedient.

APR

Verses 39–41:
Jesus thanked the Father in advance when Lazarus was still dead.

Verses 43, 44:
Only after that did He receive the fulfillment of His request.

⤲ PRAYING ACCORDING TO THE WILL OF GOD ⤳

The promises God has given us in His Word are of enormous significance for our life as Christians. The apostle Peter writes that through God's promises we will receive all we need for our Christian life and that thereby we partake of God's nature (2 Peter 1:3, 4). We could also say that through the biblical promises God has given us His grace and strength and has given us the gift that was promised. In a similar sense God's commandments are also promises. God demands nothing of us that we with His help cannot accomplish. Whatever God commands is doable by His strength. All His biddings are enablings! The apostle Paul says, "God had power to do what he had promised" (Romans 4:21). Already the Old Testament states, "He is faithful in all he does" (Psalm 33:4). There is one thing, however, that is impossible for God to do: "It is impossible for God to lie" (Hebrews 6:18). God will keep His promises! It is helpful to underline God's promises in the Bible and to memorize them so that we know them when we need them. But we have to be careful not to read our own wishes into God's promises, thereby expecting something that God did not promise at all. This will lead only to disappointment.

But when we know that our request is in full harmony with God's will because we are looking at things through God's perspective, we can be certain that He hears our prayer and that we will receive what we ask for.

---

1. You can find a full discussion of the A-B-Cs of Bible prayer in the excellent book by Glenn Coon, *The A-B-C's of Bible Prayer* (Review and Herald®, 1972).

Prayer is the opening of the heart to God as to a friend. Not that it is necessary in order to make known to God what we are, but in order to enable us to receive Him. Prayer does not bring God down to us, but brings us up to Him.

....

Ellen G. White, *Steps to Christ*, p. 93

LONGING FOR GOD

PRAYER JOURNAL
&
BIBLE JOURNAL

MAY

....

MY PRAISE · MY THANKS · MY PRAYERS

MAY

"

Beware in your prayers, above everything else, of limiting God, not only by unbelief, but by fancying that you know what He can do.

....

Andrew Murray

"

May 1

May 2

May 3

OT *1 Samuel 20–22*   May 1   *Mark 15* NT

OT *1 Samuel 23; 24*   May 2   *Mark 16* NT

OT *1 Samuel 25; 26*   May 3   *Psalm 49* Ps

MAY

MY PRAISE · MY THANKS · MY PRAYERS

MAY

66

The statement that the Bible is the worldwide best seller in the history of book publishing is an understatement.

Unknown

99

May 4

May 5

May 6

OT *1 Samuel 27; 28*   May 4   *1 Corinthians 1* NT

MAY

OT *1 Samuel 29–31*   May 5   *1 Corinthians 2* NT

OT *2 Samuel 1; 2*   May 6   *Psalm 50* Ps

66

To pray is good; it
lightens the heart.

....
F. M. Dostoyevsky

99

May 7

May 8

May 9

MAY

OT *2 Samuel 3–5*   May 7   *1 Corinthians 3* NT

MAY

OT *2 Samuel 6; 7*   May 8   *1 Corinthians 4* NT

OT *2 Samuel 8–10*   May 9   *1 Corinthians 5* NT

> We Christians are the only Bible that is being read by a large segment of the population, but I am afraid we are the worst translation.

Hans J. Eckstein

May 10

May 11

May 12

MAY

OT *2 Samuel 11; 12*   May 10   *Psalm 51* Ps

OT *2 Samuel 13; 14*   May 11   *1 Corinthians 6* NT

MAY

OT *2 Samuel 15; 16*   May 12   *1 Corinthians 7* NT

MY PRAISE · MY THANKS · MY PRAYERS

Prayer can change
a situation or, if the
situation remains the
same, can strengthen
my shoulders to help
me carry the load.

. . . .

Paul Deitenbeck

May 13

May 14

May 15

OT *2 Samuel 17; 18*   May 13   *Psalms 52–54* Ps

MAY

OT *2 Samuel 19; 20*   May 14   *1 Corinthians 8* NT

OT *2 Samuel 21; 22*   May 15   *1 Corinthians 9* NT

MY PRAISE - MY THANKS - MY PRAYERS

The Bible tells us
to love our neigh-
bors, and also to
love our enemies;
probably because
they are generally
the same people.

....

G. K. Chesterton

MAY

May 16

May 17

May 18

OT *2 Samuel 23; 24*   May 16   *1 Corinthians 10* NT

OT *1 Kings 1; 2*   May 17   *Psalm 55* Ps

OT *1 Kings 3–5*   May 18   *1 Corinthians 11* NT

MY PRAISE · MY THANKS · MY PRAYERS

66

Get into the habit
of saying, "Speak,
Lord," and life
will become a
romance.

....

Oswald Chambers

99

May 19

May 20

May 21

OT *1 Kings 6; 7*　　　　　　May 19　　　　　　*1 Corinthians 12* NT

OT *1 Kings 8; 9*　　　　　　May 20　　　　　　*Psalms 56; 57* Ps

OT *1 Kings 10; 11*　　　　　　May 21　　　　　　*1 Corinthians 13* NT

MAY

MY PRAISE - MY THANKS - MY PRAYERS

66

Most people only
know the cardboard
cover of the Bible;
and that is really
the darkest part of
this book!

....

Wolfgang Dyck

99

MAY

May 22

May 23

May 24

OT *1 Kings 12; 13*   May 22   *1 Corinthians 14* NT

OT *1 Kings 14; 15*   May 23   *1 Corinthians 15* NT

OT *1 Kings 16; 17*   May 24   *Psalms 58; 59* Ps

"

The genuine relationship in prayer does not develop when God hears what we have asked of Him but when the praying person continues in prayer until he hears what God is asking of him.

Søren Kierkegaard

"

May 25

May 26

May 27

OT *1 Kings 18; 19*   May 25   *1 Corinthians 16* NT

OT *1 Kings 20; 21*   May 26   *2 Corinthians 1* NT

OT *1 Kings 22*   May 27   *Psalms 60; 61* Ps

66

When a Christian shuns fellowship with other Christians, the devil smiles. When he stops studying the Bible, the devil laughs. When he stops praying, the devil shouts for joy.

....

Corrie ten Boom

99

May 28

May 29

May 30

May 31

GOD'S PROMISES - MY KNOWLEDGE

OT *2 Kings 1–3*   May 28   *2 Corinthians 2* NT

OT *2 Kings 4; 5*   May 29   *2 Corinthians 3* NT

OT *2 Kings 6; 7*   May 30   *2 Corinthians 4* NT

OT *2 Kings 8; 9*   May 31   *Psalms 62; 63* Ps

MORE THOUGHTS

31 REASONS
to Pray for Others

MAY

*Practical suggestions for prayer and proven suggestions
to think about your faith life*

⌒ PRAYERS FOR OTHER PEOPLE ⌒

Here you will find thirty-one suggestions on how to specifically pray for other people. The idea is to take a whole month, thirty-one days, to pray for specific things that you wish you would see in the lives of other persons. This idea developed out of my prayers for my own children. Like any believing parent regularly prays for his or her children, so I, too, included my children in my prayers. My wish was for them to be happy, that God would help them to make good decisions, that they would be successful, that they would find help in difficult situations, and that they would live under God's special protection and guidance. However, I often found myself using the same worn-out phrases in my prayers. Frequently my prayers were nothing more than a thoughtless recital of the same concerns and phrases.

During a time when, because of the death of my wife, I was confronted with extra challenges, I came across a suggestion[1] that gave the prayers for my children a new direction. The idea is to pray every day, for a whole month, for a specific character trait or a spiritual virtue that I wish would characterize my child. Praying with that focus enriched my own prayer life and intensified my relationship to my children.

I soon realized not only that this way to pray was a blessing for my own children, but also that anyone can profit by it: cousins, nephews and nieces, grandchildren, godchildren, students, the children and youth of my church, my friends and neighbors, my colleagues at work and business partners. This kind of prayer can become a blessing for every person! It was enriching for me to read the relevant Bible texts so that I could pray in the spirit of the Bible with the specific words of Scripture for a particular individual. Praying for another person by name has a life-changing quality. Actually, the list below does not only express prayer requests for other people but also challenges me to practice the same things! When I live and practice what I pray, my children and others will find my prayers genuine and authentic, and the Holy Spirit can work even more effectively.

The suggestions are based on actual biblical statements that are mentioned in the given texts. I recommend reading the texts before you pray. The following list is based on Bob Hostetler's pattern but was edited and rewritten by me. To pray for a person in a focused way, you can insert the relevant name into the blank space.

MAY

﹏ 31 REASONS ﹏

1. **Love.** "Lord, let _____ lead a life that is touched by Your love so that all areas of his/her life are directed by Your Holy Spirit who lives in him/her" (Ephesians 5:2; Galatians 5:25).

2. **Yearning for God.** "O Lord, as a deer longs for a stream of cool water, so let _____ long for You, the living God. Satisfy his/her yearning, and give him/her Your peace, which is far beyond human understanding" (Psalm 42:1, 2; Philippians 4:7).

3. **Love for God's Word.** "God, You are the God who speaks, who has created the world through Your powerful word and who has given us the written Word of God, the Bible. Please awake in _____ a love for Your Word so that it will come alive for him/her and become more desirable than fine gold" (Psalm 119:96–98; 19:10).

4. **Uprightness and Truthfulness.** "Dear God, let uprightness and truthfulness grow in the life of _____ because You are a God of truth, and you let the upright succeed" (1 Chronicles 29:17; Proverbs 2:7).

5. **Growing in Grace and Knowledge.** "Gracious Father in heaven, I ask that _____ will grow in the grace and knowledge of our Lord and Savior Jesus Christ and experience Your transforming grace today" (2 Peter 3:18).

6. **Self-Control.** "Good Lord, give _____ the gift of self-control and restraint so that he/she will not damage himself/herself through hasty and thoughtless actions. Let _____ be alert and self-disciplined in everything he/she does" (Proverbs 25:28; James 3:5; 1 Thessalonians 5:6; 2 Timothy 1:7).

7. **Righteousness.** "Righteous God, help _____ to love righteousness in the same way as You are righteous in all You do. Give _____ wisdom and skill to be just in his/her relationships with others" (Psalm 11:7; Micah 6:8).

8. **Mercy.** "Gracious and merciful Father in heaven, let _____ become a merciful person just as You are merciful" (Luke 6:36).

9. **Honor and Respect.** "Heavenly Father, give _____ a proper measure of honor and respect for others because You have created all of us in Your image" (1 Peter 2:17; Romans 12:10; 13:7).

10. **Biblical Self-Esteem.** "Creator God, help that _____ finds his/her value and dignity in the fact that You

created him/her and have re-created him/her in Jesus Christ for a life of good deeds" (Ephesians 2:10).

11. **Faithfulness.** "Faithful God, let Your faithfulness and loyalty be engraved on the heart of _____ so that he/she will never lose it and will himself/herself be inspired to be a faithful person" (Proverbs 3:3).

12. **Courage.** "Powerful God, let _____ always be strong and courageous in those things that he/she in faith does for You" (Deuteronomy 31:6; Joshua 1:9).

13. **Purity.** "God, create a pure heart in _____ and put a new and loyal spirit in him/her so that his/her pure motives will be apparent in his/her deeds" (Psalm 51:10; Galatians 2:20).

14. **Kindness.** "Our kind Savior and Father in heaven, fill _____ with kindness so that he/she will resemble You in his/her relationships with others" (Galatians 5:22; Colossians 3:12; Titus 3:4).

15. **Gladness.** "God of joy and gladness, fill _____ with joy so that he/she will practice his/her faith with gladness" (Psalm 40:16; Ecclesiastes 3:12).

16. **Helpfulness.** "God, our helper in need, give _____ the willingness to joyfully serve others in their needs and to do good with the means You have given him/her" (1 Timothy 6:18).

17. **Generosity.** "Our Father in heaven, You are a generous God who gladly gives us more than we need. Teach _____ the joy of giving and don't let him/her be penny-pinching, because You love a cheerful giver" (2 Corinthians 9:7, 8).

18. **Peace-Loving.** "Prince of Peace, give _____ the wisdom and the ability to work for peace. Let him/her do everything possible to promote peace. Fill him/her with Your shalom/peace, which is far beyond human understanding" (Matthew 5:9; Philippians 4:7; Romans 14:17).

19. **Joy.** Father in heaven, let _____ radiate with joy in his/her faith, and fill him/her with Your joy" (Psalm 34:5; Romans 15:13; 1 John 1:4).

20. **Perseverance.** "God of Abraham, Isaac, and Jacob, give _____ perseverance in the tasks You have given him/her to do. Don't let him/her get weary along the way. And give him/her clear goals. Because only those who have a worthwhile goal before their eyes will develop the perseverance to reach it" (Hebrews 12:1; Galatians 6:9).

21. **Faith.** "I pray, Father in heaven, that faith will develop deeper roots in the heart of _____ and that his/her dependence on You and Your Word will grow stronger so that he/she will receive what You have promised those who believe" (Luke 8:5–8, 11–15; Hebrews 11:1).

MAY

22. **Humility.** "Lord Jesus Christ, cultivate true humility in _____ and protect him/her from false pride. Let him/her humbly respect the other person and in love be tolerant of others" (Philippians 2:3; Ephesians 4:2; 1 Peter 5:5).

23. **Sympathy.** "Jesus Christ, You are someone who has great compassion. Give _____ the ability to sympathize with other people and to show genuine caring and empathy toward others around him/her" (Hebrews 5:2).

24. **Responsibility.** "Lord, help _____ to take responsibility for his/her own behavior and decisions. Let him/her mature into a responsible person who ultimately recognizes also his/her responsibility to You" (Romans 14:12; 1 Peter 4:5).

25. **Contentment.** "Father, teach _____ the happiness of being content with the things You have given him/her and with what he/she possesses. May You be more important to him/her than any earthly belongings" (Psalm 73:25; 2 Corinthians 12:9).

26. **Patience.** "Patient God, let _____ become more like You in practicing patience in his/her relationships with other people. Let him/her serve You with patience and learn from You because Your patient grace enables us to change" (Romans 2:4; 2 Corinthians 6:4; 2 Thessalonians 3:5; James 1:3, 4).

27. **Readiness for Service.** "God, please help _____ to serve You willingly and to do his/her work carefully with diligence and cheerfulness knowing that it is ultimately about serving You rather than to impress others" (Ephesians 6:7; Colossians 3:23).

28. **Hope.** "God of hope, fill the faith of _____ with joy and peace so that the biblical hope in his/her life will continue to grow through the power of the Holy Spirit" (Romans 15:13; Psalm 28:7).

29. **Gratitude.** "Gracious God, help _____ to learn and appreciate gratitude so that his/her thoughts are filled with gratitude for everything You have done" (Colossians 2:7; 1 Thessalonians 5:18).

30. **A Heart for Mission.** "Lord of the nations, King of kings, let _____ feel a desire to witness to others and to joyfully share his/her faith with the whole world" (Matthew 9:37, 38; Psalm 96:3).

31. **Surrender of the Life to Jesus Christ.** "God of life, through faith in Jesus Christ You are giving us eternal life. Through the Holy Spirit move the thoughts and the will of _____ so that he/she recognizes that he/she needs You and can only have fullness of life with You" (John 14:6; 6:68, 69; Romans 3:23, 24; Philippians 2:13).

---

1. Bob Hostetler, "31 Biblical Virtues to Pray for Your Children," in Dean Ridings, *The Pray! Prayer Journal: Daily Steps Toward Praying God's Heart* (Colorado Springs: NavPress, 2003), 99, 100.

PRAYER to the Great Physician for the healing of the soul brings the blessing of God. PRAYER unites us one to another and to God. PRAYER brings Jesus to our side, and gives new strength and fresh grace to the fainting, perplexed soul. By PRAYER the sick have been encouraged to believe that God will look with compassion upon them. A ray of light penetrates to the hopeless soul, and becomes a savor of life unto life. PRAYER has "subdued kingdoms, wrought righteousness, obtained promises, stopped the mouths of lions, quenched the violence of fire."

Ellen G. White, *Advent Review and Sabbath Herald*, Feb. 30, 1900

LONGING FOR GOD

PRAYER JOURNAL
&
BIBLE JOURNAL

JUNE

66

Let all your actions
be consistent with
your prayers, and
be in fact a cont-
inuation of your
prayers.

....

C. H. Spurgeon

99

JUN

June 1

June 2

June 3

OT *2 Kings 10–12*   June 1   *2 Corinthians 5* NT

OT *2 Kings 13; 14*   June 2   *2 Corinthians 6* NT

OT *2 Kings 15; 16*   June 3   *Psalms 64; 65* Ps

66

Prayer is the key to
the Bible. It is the
only one that fits.

. . . .

Hans Bruns

99

JUN

June 4

June 5

June 6

OT *2 Kings 17; 18*　　　June 4　　　*2 Corinthians 7* NT

OT *2 Kings 19; 20*　　　June 5　　　*2 Corinthians 8* NT

JUN

OT *2 Kings 21; 22*　　　June 6　　　*2 Corinthians 9* NT

66

It is not a haphazard thing, but in the constitution of God, that there are certain times of the day when it not only seems easier, but it *is* easier, to meet God. If you have ever prayed in the dawn you will ask yourself why you were so foolish as not to do it always.

....

Oswald Chambers

99

JUN

June 7

June 8

June 9

OT *2 Kings 23–25*   June 7   *Psalms 66; 67* Ps

_____

_____

_____

_____

_____

_____

_____

OT *1 Chronicles 1–3*   June 8   *2 Corinthians 10* NT

_____

_____

_____

_____

_____

_____

_____

OT *1 Chronicles 4–6*   June 9   *2 Corinthians 11* NT

_____

_____

_____

_____

_____

_____

_____

> To lose the Bible does not mean we lose our education and our language; it means we lose our life.
>
> ....
> Gerhard Ebeling

JUN

June 10

June 11

June 12

OT *1 Chronicles 7–10*　　　　　June 10　　　　　*Psalm 68* Ps

_____
_____
_____
_____
_____
_____
_____

OT *1 Chronicles 11–14*　　　　　June 11　　　　　*2 Corinthians 12* NT

JUN

_____
_____
_____
_____
_____
_____
_____

OT *1 Chronicles 15; 16*　　　　　June 12　　　　　*2 Corinthians 13* NT

_____
_____
_____
_____
_____
_____
_____

MY PRAISE · MY THANKS · MY PRAYERS

66

We should not pray
as if we were reading
from a letter.

....

Talmud

99

June 13

June 14

June 15

OT *1 Chronicles 17; 18*   June 13   *Galatians 1* NT

OT *1 Chronicles 19–21*   June 14   *Psalm 69* Ps

OT *1 Chronicles 22; 23*   June 15   *Galatians 2* NT

> To become adult Christians, you have to familiarize yourself with the Bible.

J. Chrysostomus

JUN

June 16

June 17

June 18

OT *1 Chronicles 24–27*   June 16   *Galatians 3* NT

OT *1 Chronicles 28; 29*   June 17   *Psalms 70; 71* Ps

JUN

OT *2 Chronicles 1; 2*   June 18   *Galatians 4* NT

66

Our prayers should be short and right to the point. Let the long, tiresome petitions be left for the closet, if any have such to offer.

....

Ellen G. White, *Testimonies for the Church*, vol. 4, p. 71

99

JUN

June 19

June 20

June 21

OT *2 Chronicles 3–5*   June 19   *Galatians 5* NT

OT *2 Chronicles 6; 7*   June 20   *Galatians 6* NT

OT *2 Chronicles 8; 9*   June 21   *Psalm 72* Ps

66

The Bible is like a field that can never be harvested enough and thus never lies waste and empty. It is like a spring that flows continually and that flows ever more abundantly the more you dip out of it.

....

Ephraim the Syrian

99

JUN

June 22

June 23

June 24

OT *2 Chronicles 10–12* June 22 *Ephesians 1* NT

OT *2 Chronicles 13–15* June 23 *Ephesians 2* NT

JUN

OT *2 Chronicles 16; 17* June 24 *Psalm 73* Ps

66

He who calls on
God does not need a
cell phone.

....

Pater Madison
alias Klaus Klages

99

June 25

June 26

June 27

OT *2 Chronicles 18–20*   June 25   *Ephesians 3* NT

OT *2 Chronicles 21–23*   June 26   *Ephesians 4* NT

JUN

OT *2 Chronicles 24; 25*   June 27   *Ephesians 5* NT

"

Christ is God's strength and God's wisdom, and he who does not know Holy Scriptures knows neither God's strength nor His wisdom; to not know the Scriptures means to not know Christ.

Hieronymus

"

June 28

June 29

June 30

OT *2 Chronicles 26–28*　　　　June 28　　　　*Psalm 74* Ps

OT *2 Chronicles 29; 30*　　　　June 29　　　　*Ephesians 6* NT

JUN

OT *2 Chronicles 31; 32*　　　　June 30　　　　*Luke 1:1–38* NT

MORE THOUGHTS

PRAYING
and Fasting

JUNE

*Practical suggestions for prayer and proven suggestions
to think about your faith life*

John Wesley once said, "The man who never fasts is no more in the way to heaven than the man who never prays."[1] The Bible often mentions fasting in connection with prayer. Jesus fasted before He started His public ministry (Matthew 4:2; Luke 4:2). The apostles prayed and fasted to gain assurance that Paul and Barnabas should be sent out as missionaries (Acts 13:2, 3). In the Old Testament, fasting was also a common practice among believing men and women (1 Kings 21:9, 12; 2 Chronicles 20:3; Ezra 8:21; Esther 4:3, 16; Isaiah 58:5, 6; Jeremiah 36:9; Daniel 9:3; Joel 2:12; Jonah 3:5; etc.).

In contrast to wellness fasting, biblical fasting is not about observing a specific diet that is supposed to aid in weight loss or that is intended to increase a sense of well-being. Rather, it has to do with conscientiously setting aside specific time for concentration on prayer and communion with God.[2] Fasting does not create faith. Faith grows in us as we read, hear, and dwell upon God's Word. Fasting, however, has the capacity to encourage and strengthen faith in the person who is involved in this discipline. This does not mean that the one who eats the least has the most faith. Such an understanding is untrue and extremist. It simply means that fasting as an exercise of self-denial has certain benefits, and one of them can be seen in an increase of spiritual alertness and sensitivity.[3]

Fasting is the deliberate decision to temporarily abstain from food and distracting activities for a specific period of time to deepen one's spiritual life. By abstaining from the familiar daily routine that captivates much of our energies and attention, one gains new spiritual freedom. Through fasting and prayer the focus of one's daily life changes: my own daily concern for food, my attention to what I do that captivates so much of my time and energy, receives a timeout that allows an unhurried and obedient listening to what God has to say. Biblical fasting is not primarily about me or other people but about my relationship to God (see the thoughts in the chapter "Prayer That Pleases God").

The English word *to fast* is related to the word *to fasten* and originally meant "to fasten something down." In the old gothic language it had a double meaning: (a) to hold fast, to preserve, to observe; and (b) to fast in the sense of abstaining from food.[4]

In the Bible, the Greek New Testament word for *to fast* is *nesteuein*, which means "fasting, not having had to eat." It expresses the act of going without food for a devotional purpose.[5] When I voluntarily give up established habits and loosen the ties that bind me to the material world and my eating, I can become more spiritually awake and alert. The fixation on what I eat, watch, listen to, touch, and make is interrupted. My vision is turned from the routines of my little human world to God's eternal world, for "in nothing is man more closely connected with the world of sense than in this need for, and enjoyment of, food. It was the fruit with which man was tempted and fell in Paradise. It was with bread that Jesus was tempted in the wilderness. But He triumphed in fasting. . . . Fasting helps to express, to deepen, and to confirm the resolution that we are ready to sacrifice anything, even ourselves, to attain the Kingdom of God."[6]

By giving up food I signal that I as a human being do not live by bread alone but by every word that proceeds from the mouth of God (Matthew 4:4). When I am fasting, my thinking can become clearer and more composed. Moreover, the genuine fast looks to God and does not cast a glance at other people (Matthew 6:16–18).

ᴄᴏ FASTING THAT PLEASES GOD ᴈ

Fasting that pleases God intensifies prayer and my energy to serve my neighbor. I am able to hear God's word without distraction and gain a new willingness to turn it into action. My faith and trust in God's loving guidance grows. I become more sensitive toward the concerns and needs of others. Often a greater perception of spiritual things also leads to a deeper knowledge of myself. When I fast, I become more mindful of my own spiritual situation. That in turn helps me to recognize God's will more clearly and to be able to better distinguish good from evil (Hebrews 5:14). Through my obedient praying and fasting I give the Holy Spirit the opportunity to change me and to work on me and through me more intensively.

Thus, biblical fasting is an expression of my humility before God, which reveals that I am truly dependent on Him and that I am consciously seeking His presence. As such it becomes an effective force against Satan and turns into a powerful tool that God can use to accomplish amazing things. Here are two examples from the Bible:

When God's people faced specific times of need (e.g., famine), God said, "Return to me with all your heart, with fasting and weeping and mourning" (Joel 2:12). Through fasting we express our hope in God's intervention.

When the people of God needed protection and deliverance, they fasted and prayed. Thus, the young Esther through her courageous appearance before the Persian king Artaxerxes saved the Jews from the heinous destruction. Together with all the other Jews she prepared herself for this decisive encounter with the king by fasting for three days (Esther 4:16).

⌒ FASTING DOES NOT CHANGE GOD; IT CHANGES ME ⌒

In contrast to hunger, fasting is the *deliberate* abstention from something that actually is available to me. Through fasting I want to consciously create undisturbed time for God that would otherwise be filled with other things. As such, fasting should not "be confined to the question of food and drink; fasting should really be made to include abstinence from anything which is legitimate in and of itself for the sake of some special spiritual purpose."[7] I can also for a specified time relinquish television, the Internet, e-mail, Facebook, Twitter, Instagram, my cell phone, and so forth to create time to concentrate on God and His Word.

As mentioned earlier, fasting does not create faith. Faith grows in us as we read, hear, and dwell upon God's Word. Fasting, however, has the capacity to encourage faith in the person who is involved in this discipline. If you want to begin a fast, examine your motives according to Matthew 6:33. True fasting resists the subtle temptation to win God's approval for one's own concerns and to manipulate Him. God cannot be forced to act because I am fasting. Rather, God wants to give Himself to me in love. In this, His generosity cannot be surpassed. But in His generous love and grace God remains sovereign. HE decides what He is going to give to whom and when. Fasting does not change God—it changes me! It puts me into right relationship with God. Fasting that pleases God is worth a try. Try it out sometime.

The spirit of true fasting and prayer is the spirit
which yields mind, heart, and will to God.
—Ellen G. White, *Counsels on Diet and Foods*, p. 189

JUN

1. John Wesley, "Causes of Inefficacy of Christianity," *Sermons on Several Occasions*, ed. Thomas Jackson, vol. 2 (New York: T. Mason and G. Lane, 1840), 440, as quoted in John Piper, *A Hunger for God: Desiring God Through Fasting and Prayer* (Wheaton, IL: Crossway Books, 1997), 191.

2. I base my ideas on valuable thoughts from the article by Andreas Kusch, "Beten und Fasten: Eine biblische Orientierung und Anleitung," in *Brennpunkt Seelsorge* 1/2010: 4–13. This issue contains additional valuable suggestions on the subject of prayer and fasting.

3. See David R. Smith, *Fasting: A Neglected Discipline* (Fort Washington, PA: Christian Literature Crusade, 1954), 47, 48, as quoted in Piper, *A Hunger for God*, 201.

4. See Friso Melzer, *Das Wort in den Wörtern. Die deutsche Sprache im Dienste der Christusnachfolge: ein theo-philosophisches Wörterbuch* (Tübingen: J. C. B. Mohr [Paul Siebeck], 1965), 124.

5. William Arndt, Frederick W. Danker, and Walter Bauer, *A Greek-English Lexicon of the New Testament and Other Early Christian Literature* (Chicago: University of Chicago Press, 2000), 671.

6. Andrew Murray, *With Christ in the School of Prayer* (Springdale, PA: Whitaker House, 1981), 100, 101, as quoted in Piper, *A Hunger for God*, 197, 198.

7. Martyn Lloyd-Jones, *Studies in the Sermon on the Mount*, vol. 2 (Grand Raids, MI: Eerdmans, 1960), 38, as quoted in Piper, *A Hunger for God*, 200.

LONGING FOR GOD

PRAYER JOURNAL
&
BIBLE JOURNAL

JULY

> 66
>
> Prayer helps you to stand erect because it takes a burden off of you.
>
> ....
> Peter Hahne
>
> 99

July 1

July 2

July 3

OT *2 Chronicles 33; 34*   July 1   *Psalms 75; 76* Ps

OT *2 Chronicles 35; 36*   July 2   *Luke 1:39–80* NT

OT *Ezra 1; 2*   July 3   *Luke 2* NT

MY PRAISE · MY THANKS · MY PRAYERS

> When we give thanks we give God the glory for what He has done for us; and when we worship or give praise, we give God glory for what He is in Himself.

O. Hallesby

July 4

July 5

July 6

OT *Ezra 3; 4*   July 4   *Luke 3* NT

OT *Ezra 5; 6*   July 5   *Psalm 77* Ps

OT *Ezra 7; 8*   July 6   *Luke 4* NT

66

Prayer means
confiding in God.

....

Dietrich Bonhoeffer

99

July 7

July 8

July 9

OT *Ezra 9; 10*   July 7   *Luke 5* NT

_____
_____
_____
_____
_____
_____
_____
_____
_____

OT *Nehemiah 1; 2*   July 8   *Psalm 78:1–37* Ps

_____
_____
_____
_____
_____
_____
_____
_____
_____

JUL

OT *Nehemiah 3; 4*   July 9   *Luke 6* NT

_____
_____
_____
_____
_____
_____
_____
_____
_____

66

When you go to bed at night, take a thought from the Holy Scriptures to bed with you to consider it in your heart—to ruminate on it like an animal—and to gently fall asleep with it. It should not be too much, rather a small portion, but well thought through and understood. And when you rise in the morning, you will find it as the harvest of the previous day.

....

Martin Luther

99

JUL

July 10

July 11

July 12

OT *Nehemiah 5; 6*

July 10

Luke 7 NT

OT *Nehemiah 7; 8*

July 11

Luke 8 NT

OT *Nehemiah 9; 10*

July 12

Psalm 78:38–72 Ps

66

Tell me to whom
you pray when
things are going well,
and I will tell you
how pious you are.

. . . .

Kurt Tucholsky

99

July 13

July 14

July 15

OT *Nehemiah 11; 12*   July 13   *Luke 9* NT

OT *Nehemiah 13*   July 14   *Luke 10* NT

JUL

OT *Esther 1–3*   July 15   *Psalm 79* Ps

> 66
>
> It is just as impossible to understand the Bible with your intellect as it is to empty the ocean with your hand.
>
> ....
> Otto von Bismarck
>
> 99

July 16

July 17

July 18

OT *Esther 4; 5*   July 16   *Luke 11* NT

_____

_____

_____

_____

_____

_____

OT *Esther 6; 7*   July 17   *Luke 12* NT

_____

_____

_____

_____

_____

_____

JUL

OT *Esther 8–10*   July 18   *Luke 13* NT

_____

_____

_____

_____

_____

_____

> **66**
>
> He who
> kneels the
> most, stands
> the best.
>
> ·········
>
> Dwight Moody
>
> **99**

July 19

July 20

July 21

JUL

OT *Job 1; 2*　　　　　July 19　　　　　*Psalm 80* Ps

OT *Job 3; 4*　　　　　July 20　　　　　*Luke 14* NT

JUL

OT *Job 5; 6*　　　　　July 21　　　　　*Luke 15* NT

Gather the riches
of God's promises.
Nobody can take
away from you those
texts from the Bible
which you have
learned by heart.

....

Corrie ten Boom

July 22

July 23

July 24

OT *Job 7; 8* July 22 *Psalms 81; 82* Ps

OT *Job 9; 10* July 23 *Luke 16* NT

OT *Job 11; 12* July 24 *Luke 17* NT

66

Prayer is incense that gives the devil a headache.

....

(A proverb)

99

July 25

July 26

July 27

OT *Job 13; 14* July 25 *Luke 18* NT

_____
_____
_____
_____
_____
_____
_____

OT *Job 15–17* July 26 *Psalms 83; 84* Ps

_____
_____
_____
_____
_____
_____
_____

OT *Job 18; 19* July 27 *Luke 19* NT

_____
_____
_____
_____
_____
_____
_____

JUL

"

When people do
not find Jesus in
the Bible, it is their
own fault; however
if they do not find
Him in your life,
then it is your fault.

. . . .

F. V. Bodelschwingh

"

JUL

July 28

July 29

July 30

July 31

OT *Job 20; 21*   July 28   *Luke 20* NT

OT *Job 22; 23*   July 29   *Psalm 85* Ps

JUL

OT *Job 24–26*   July 30   *Luke 21* NT

OT *Job 27; 28*   July 31   *Luke 22* NT

MORE THOUGHTS

·······················

PRAYER

and Our Waiting for an Answer

JULY

✕

Practical suggestions for prayer and proven suggestions
to think about your faith life

Who has not had this experience: You pray and wait for an answer. And you wait. And you pray. And you wait—for a very long time, and you don't seem to receive what you've been praying for. Even when we pray sincere prayers and in our prayers ask God for things He approves of, it can happen that God lets us wait. To persevere in prayer is a lesson that people through all ages have had to learn. God does not want spiritual weaklings who are easily discouraged. He wants sincere people who trustingly claim His promises and who are persevering in their prayers. From a biblical perspective the primary purpose of waiting is to bring to light who I am and who I am becoming while I am waiting. The experience of waiting confronts me with a significant spiritual decision: Do I allow my impatience and my doubts to question God's goodness and omnipotence? Or do I recognize that in waiting I am confronted with a unique opportunity that will help me to become the person God wishes me to be? Perhaps through waiting I will become someone whom I never would have been otherwise. If we look at it this way, waiting becomes God's means of transformation to change me according to His will. Thus, waiting is truly an expression of God's goodness and grace. It helps me to become more like God because God also waits in His great patience since He does not want anyone to be lost who could still be saved.[1]

While we are waiting for God to answer our prayers, it can happen that worries and uncertainties sneak up on us, especially when we have been praying for a long time and the answer to our prayers is delayed.

Maybe it will help you to understand that we go through several stages while we are waiting for answers to our prayers.[2]

❧ INTENSITY ❧

The beginning of a prayer request is often characterized by a certain degree of *intensity*. A crisis or special need often stimulates me to focus all my energy on asking God for help and for a solution to the problem. This is the first intensive stage.

DISTRACTION

However, it is very difficult to maintain such an intense attitude of prayer over a longer period of time. Everyday life and essential daily transactions inevitably distract my heart and my thoughts and necessarily lead me to turn to other things that are essential for my living and survival. Therefore, *distraction* characterizes the second stage because everyday life with its daily routine goes on.

ANGER AND IMPATIENCE

In the third phase we often experience *anger and impatience* because the desired answer does not appear in the form we had hoped for or because it is delayed. When anger arises, it is often directed at God because He seemingly does not interfere or He apparently does not help. Our anger may also turn toward the cause of the problem because the problem does not disappear and continues to cause distress. Or anger turns against myself because I am unable to do anything about the situation or might feel responsible for it.

ACCUSATION

This anger often leads to a form of *accusation*. In this fourth phase of the waiting process we sometimes reproach God: Why don't You act faster? Why is nothing happening? Why don't You step in to solve the problem? Sometimes accusations are turned toward others whom we perceive to be the cause of the problem. Or I accuse myself because Satan, the accuser of all human beings, insinuates that God has delayed the answer to my prayer because I am so sinful or unworthy.

DISCOURAGEMENT

In the fifth phase anger and accusation often lead to frustrations and *discouragement*. I become uncertain whether and how I should continue to pray. If Satan succeeds in discouraging me, he has succeeded. God never discourages us. Instead, God longs to help me because He tenderly loves me! This important insight leads into the next phase.

⌒ DETERMINATION ⌒

If I don't let anger and frustration discourage me, I will advance to the next phase in which I *determine* to continue to pray. Sometimes I may feel like the man who calls out, "I believe; help my unbelief!" (Mark 9:24, NKJV). Sometimes I might wrestle like Jacob and cry, "I will not let You go unless You bless me!" (Genesis 32:26, NKJV). Faith in this new phase is not so much a feeling but a conscious determination not to give up praying no matter how and when God will answer the prayer (Romans 12:12). This experience is possible only when I trust that God really is good and that He has kind intentions toward me. It pays to trust God and to wait on Him, "casting all your care upon Him, for He cares for you" (1 Peter 5:7, NKJV). When my praying passes this test, then the next phase is able to start.

⌒ JOY AND INNER PEACE ⌒

Overcoming the temptation of discouragement in prayer opens the way for *rejoicing* in hope (Romans 12:12; 15:13; Philippians 4:4). A joyful faith, in turn, results in a heart that is filled with a *peace* that is higher than any human understanding. This is how I can learn to trust in God even if from a human standpoint I cannot imagine how God can accomplish the thing. The peace of God is grounded in the certainty that God's word is dependable and deserves full acceptance (1 Timothy 1:15; 4:9; 2 Timothy 2:11; Hebrews 2:3).

In each of these stages God's help is available to me! With His help it is possible to have a new experience in my prayer life! And consider: It is *always* too soon to stop praying! It is *never* too late to start praying!

---

1. See Frank M. Hasel, "Waiting: God's Way of Transformation," *Adventist World*, October 2011, 12, 13.

2. The following stages are adapted from Ron Susek, "7 Waiting Phases," in *Pray*, Issue 28, p. 18, as quoted in Dean Ridings, *The Pray! Prayer Journal* (Colorado Springs, CO: NavPress, 2003), 104, 105.

LONGING FOR GOD

························

PRAYER JOURNAL
&
BIBLE JOURNAL

AUGUST

✕

66

Praying means asking for a renewal of personal strength from God's abundance.

....

Paul Deitenbeck

99

AUG

August 1

August 2

August 3

GOD'S PROMISES - MY KNOWLEDGE

OT *Job 29; 30* August 1 *Luke 23* NT

OT *Job 31; 32* August 2 *Psalms 86; 87* Ps

AUG

OT *Job 33; 34* August 3 *Luke 24* NT

> In the Bible God Himself speaks with us as a man with his friend.
>
> ....
>
> Martin Luther

August 4

August 5

Dear Heavenly Father,
wow! you have always been around and nothing is hidden from you. Thank you for this book thank you for a Bible, a family, kids etc..

August 6

OT *Job 35; 36*   August 4   *Philippians 1* NT

OT *Job 37; 38*   August 5   *Psalm 88* NT

These chapters were about God's
sovreignty and control over
everything. Wow! There is so little
we know. God you are vast
and amazing ♡ God is in
control. Everything ♡

This was a sad psalm but
solidified the truth about
the state of the dead.

OT *Job 39; 40*   August 6   *Philippians 2* NT

AUG

66

If God had granted all the silly prayers I've made in my life, where should I be now?

. . . .
C. S. Lewis

99

August 7

August 8

August 9

OT *Job 41; 42*   August 7   *Philippians 3* NT

OT *Proverbs 1; 2*   August 8   *Philippians 4* NT

AUG

OT *Proverbs 3; 4*   August 9   *Psalm 89* Ps

MY PRAISE · MY THANKS · MY PRAYERS

66

The big news of
the Bible is not
that you love God
but that God loves
you; not that you
can know God but
that God already
knows you!

....
Max Lucado

99

August 10

August 11

August 12

AUG

GOD'S PROMISES - MY KNOWLEDGE

OT *Proverbs 5; 6* August 10 *Colossians 1* NT

OT *Proverbs 7; 8* August 11 *Colossians 2* NT

AUG

OT *Proverbs 9; 10* August 12 *Psalm 90* Ps

66

Prayer plumes the wings of God's young eaglets, that they may learn to mount above the clouds. Prayer girds the loins of God's warriors and sends them forth to combat with their sinews braced and their muscles firm.

....

C. H. Spurgeon

99

August 13

August 14

August 15

OT *Proverbs 11; 12*   August 13   *Colossians 3* NT

_____

_____

_____

_____

_____

_____

_____

OT *Proverbs 13; 14*   August 14   *Colossians 4* NT

_____

_____

_____

_____

_____

_____

_____

OT *Proverbs 15; 16*   August 15   *1 Thessalonians 1* NT

_____

_____

_____

_____

_____

_____

_____

AUG

August 16

August 17

August 18 God thank you for your kindness, faithfulness and forgiveness toward me. Lord you are a wonderful kind God. Please forgive me for my selfishness Please forgive me for my anger and waste. God you have been so good to me. Heavenly Father, please help the people in Afghanistan. Please God, please! Father please prepare me and others for your soon return.

OT *Proverbs 17; 18*　　　　　　August 16　　　　　　*Psalm 91* Ps

OT *Proverbs 19; 20*　　　　　　August 17　　　　　*1 Thessalonians 2* NT

OT *Proverbs 21; 22*　　　　　　August 18　　　　*1 Thessalonians 3* NT

Proverbs 21:30 There
is no wisdom nor understanding
nor counsel that is against
the Lord.
God you alone are right
and wise. Am I making
a mistake to do daycare?
Proverbs 22: 24, 25

v.12 please Lord make me abound
in love, establish me unblameable
in holiness before God, Even our
Father, at the coming of our Lord
Christ Jesus

66

Is prayer your
steering wheel or
your spare tire?

....

Corrie ten Boom

99

AUG

August 19

August 20

August 21

GOD'S PROMISES - MY KNOWLEDGE

OT *Proverbs 23; 24*   August 19   *Psalms 92; 93*   Ps

OT *Proverbs 25; 26*   August 20   *1 Thessalonians 4* NT

OT *Proverbs 27; 28*   August 21   *1 Thessalonians 5* NT

"

About the meaning of all things, about the meaning of sickness, of life and death, of the world, man, and history, science can tell us nothing; the Bible alone can do that.

Paul Tournier

"

August 22

August 23

August 24

OT *Proverbs 29; 30*   August 22   *2 Thessalonians 1* NT

OT *Proverbs 31*   August 23   *Psalm 94* Ps

AUG

OT *Ecclesiastes 1–3*   August 24   *2 Thessalonians 2* NT

"

Heaven's great harbour of refuge is All-prayer. Thousands of weather-beaten vessels have found a haven there, and the moment a storm comes on it is wise for us to make for it with all sail.

....

C. H. Spurgeon

"

August 25

August 26

August 27

OT *Ecclesiastes 4; 5*　　　　　　August 25　　　　　　*2 Thessalonians 3* NT

_____

OT *Ecclesiastes 6; 7*　　　　　　August 26　　　　　　*Psalms 95; 96* Ps

_____

AUG

OT *Ecclesiastes 8; 9*　　　　　　August 27　　　　　　*1 Timothy 1* NT

_____

66

The Bible is like an instruction manual for our life that applies to each age, to each vital question, and each circumstance.

....

Bernhard Langer

99

AUG

August 28

August 29

August 30

August 31

OT *Ecclesiastes 10; 11*   August 28   *1 Timothy 2* NT

OT *Ecclesiastes 12*   August 29   *1 Timothy 3* NT

OT *Song of Solomon 1; 2*   August 30   *Psalms 97; 98*   Ps

OT *Song of Solomon 3; 4*   August 31   *1 Timothy 4* NT

MORE THOUGHTS

························

BECOMING FREE
of BITTERNESS

AUGUST

✕

*Practical suggestions for prayer and proven suggestions
to think about your faith life*

Feelings of bitterness arise when anger takes hold in me, when I feel I have been treated unjustly, when things do not happen as I wish them to, when I am passed over, or when wrongdoing is not forgiven.[1] Even though I know that bitterness is not right—"for the wrath of man does not produce the righteousness of God" (James 1:20, NKJV; also cf. Titus 3:2; Philippians 4:5)—I realize that bitterness nevertheless exists in my heart and my thoughts. Even if outwardly I can control my feelings, in the long run, my bitterness does not remain unnoticed. Like water, it finds a way out and leaves behind tracks. Dirty tracks.

In Hebrews 12:15 we read about the "root of bitterness" (NKJV), which strives to spring up. From roots grow big bushes or even trees. They grow and multiply. The problem with bitterness is that it does not stay as it is. It multiplies. Like cancer that grows and spreads vigorously, bitterness increases and distorts my view of reality. Like polluted air, it stinks and affects not only myself but all those who come in contact with me. Bitterness also chains me to the past. Thus, discord and bondage result and many are defiled by bitterness (Hebrews 12:15).

↶ BITTERNESS IS NO TRIFLE ↷

Bitterness is no trifle. It is no less serious than gross visible sins. It can cause great damage in the soul of the individual as well as in the surrounding community.

How can I overcome the power of bitterness? Notice the first part of the text in Hebrews 12:15: "Looking carefully lest anyone fall short of the grace of God" (NKJV). Bitterness always starts with a lack of grace. But mind you: if there is a lack of grace, it is always my fault, never God's. With God, grace is never scarce. John writes, "And of His fullness we have all received, and grace for grace" (John 1:16, NKJV). Paul notes in Romans 5:20, "But where sin abounded, grace abounded much more" (NKJV). No matter what happened in your life—God has enough grace available for you! His grace is abundant (1 Timothy 1:14); indeed, there are "riches of His grace" (Ephesians 1:7, NKJV; cf. 2:7).

Our Father in heaven has created all the conditions that make it possible that the power of sin, and along with it all bitterness, anger, wrath, hurt feelings, and so forth, does not need to control my life. In 2 Corinthians 9:8 Paul writes, "And God is able to make all grace abound toward you, that you, always having all sufficiency in all things, may have an abundance for every good work" (NKJV).

The question is: Do I really live by grace or has a spirit of retaliation taken hold of me that makes me judge others? According to Romans 3:14, bitterness is a characteristic of the person who does not know God. When I live in bitterness, my relationship with God is disrupted, and my relationships with others suffer and are damaged. That is the reason why bitterness is listed first in the "catalog of vices" in Ephesians 4:31: "Let all bitterness, wrath, anger, clamor, and evil speaking be put away from you, with all malice" (NKJV).

The next verse shows the way to overcome bitterness: "And be kind to one another, tenderhearted, forgiving one another, even as God in Christ forgave you" (Ephesians 4:32, NKJV). Bitterness and revenge are replaced by kindness, tenderheartedness, and forgiveness. Because Christ has forgiven you, you should not withhold forgiveness from others. Kindness, tenderheartedness, and willingness to forgive are not human efforts or a discipline that God demands of me. That would be righteousness by works! They are a gift of the Holy Spirit: "But the fruit of the Spirit is love, joy, peace, longsuffering, kindness, goodness, faithfulness, gentleness, self-control" (Galatians 5:22, 23, NKJV).

However, I am able to quench the work of the Holy Spirit (1 Thessalonians 5:19). Ephesians 4:30 makes it clear that I can grieve the Holy Spirit who wants to produce this fruit in me. Immediately after this important statement the apostle Paul gives the admonition to put away all bitterness. Bitterness saddens God. That is the reason Paul charges us, "Do not let the sun go down on your wrath, nor give place to the devil" (Ephesians 4:26, 27, NKJV). When I harbor bitterness and anger, I allow the devil to have a hold of me. That is why it is so important to let go of bitterness as soon as possible.

The text in Hebrews is meant to be preventive. I should not even become bitter. But what can I do when I notice that roots of bitterness have already grown in me? The answer is: I need to remove the roots as quickly as possible before they grow into weeds or scrubs. At the very moment when a bitter thought against someone crops up, go to Jesus. Tell Him what you are feeling. Be honest with yourself and with God. When you admit having bitter feelings, you find forgiveness in God. Consider this thought: anger is not always unjustified; but bitterness is always sinful. A bitter heart has grown crooked and is incapable of changing. But God gives us the willingness to forgive. He works in us both to will and to do (Philippians 2:13). He is the best heart surgeon and a specialist to free you from your bitter feelings if you will allow it and if you ask Him to: "Create in me a clean heart, O God, and renew a steadfast spirit within me" (Psalm 51:10, NKJV). That is a prayer that pleases God and that He certainly will answer.

What should I do if whole trees, maybe even whole forests, of bitterness have already grown in me? When not only one sundown has passed, but when I have harbored bitterness for months and perhaps years? Go to God. Ask HIM to treat the root problem. Confess your sin. Ask Jesus for forgiveness and inner peace. Under no circumstances should you hold on to your bitterness, because it will damage you, others, and God's reputation.

The following steps and principles can help you to improve your life rather than to grow bitter:

1. Admit the problem.

2. Stop harboring and nurturing bitterness. You do not have the right to do that.

3. Stop making excuses for what has happened.

4. Live in the knowledge that God has forgiven you, and pass it on to others.

5. Be the one who takes the first step toward reconciliation.

6. Ask God for healing of the root problem, and with His help get rid of any trace of bitterness as soon as possible.

7. Put your intentions into actions.

8. Recognize that for God nothing is impossible.

AUG

---

1. The thoughts in this section are taken from notes that my wife put together for a women's retreat before she died. I was not able to verify any other original sources she might have used or depended on.

LONGING FOR GOD

PRAYER JOURNAL
&
BIBLE JOURNAL

SEPTEMBER

MY PRAISE · MY THANKS · MY PRAYERS

> Prayer is the opening of the heart to God as to a friend. Not that it is necessary in order to make known to God what we are, but in order to enable us to receive Him. Prayer does not bring God down to us, but brings us up to Him.

Ellen G. White,
Steps to Christ,. p. 93

September 1

September 2

September 3

GOD'S PROMISES - MY KNOWLEDGE

OT *Song of Solomon 5; 6* September 1 *1 Timothy 5* NT

_____
_____
_____
_____
_____
_____
_____

OT *Song of Solomon 7; 8* September 2 *Psalms 99–101* Ps

_____
_____
_____
_____
_____
_____
_____

SEP

OT *Isaiah 1; 2* September 3 *1 Timothy 6* NT

_____
_____
_____
_____
_____
_____

> The existence of the Bible, as a book for the people, is the greatest benefit which the human race has ever experienced. Every attempt to belittle it is a crime against humanity.

Immanuel Kant

September 4

September 5

September 6

OT *Isaiah 3–5*   September 4   *2 Timothy 1* NT

OT *Isaiah 6; 7*   September 5   *2 Timothy 2* NT

SEP

OT *Isaiah 8; 9*   September 6   *Psalm 102* Ps

66

The wish to pray is a
prayer in itself.

....

Georges Bernanos

99

September 7

September 8

September 9

SEP

OT *Isaiah 10–12*   September 7   *2 Timothy 3* NT

OT *Isaiah 13; 14*   September 8   *2 Timothy 4* NT

SEP

OT *Isaiah 15; 16*   September 9   *Psalm 103* Ps

66

In the entire Bible it is constantly apparent that not just the hearing of the Word of God is important but especially the living it.

....

Rainer Baum

99

September 10

September 11

September 12

OT *Isaiah 17–20*   **September 10**   *Titus 1* NT

OT *Isaiah 21; 22*   **September 11**   *Titus 2* NT

SEP

OT *Isaiah 23; 24*   **September 12**   *Titus 3* NT

66

We look upon prayer simply as a means of geting things for ourselves, but the biblical purpose of prayer is that we may get to know God Himself.

....

Oswald Chambers

99

September 13

September 14

September 15

SEP

OT *Isaiah 25; 26* **September 13** *Psalm 104* Ps

OT *Isaiah 27; 28* **September 14** *Philemon* NT

SEP

OT *Isaiah 29; 30* **September 15** *Hebrews 1* NT

66

Shift from your mind conquering the Bible, down into surrender to the Spirit of God who will whisper to you what He meant by what He wrote.

. . . .

Martha Kilpatrick

99

September 16

September 17

September 18

OT *Isaiah 31; 32*   September 16   *Psalm 105*   Ps

OT *Isaiah 33; 34*   September 17   *Hebrews 2* NT

OT *Isaiah 35; 36*   September 18   *Hebrews 3* NT

SEP

66

We pray not in order
to report to the
Father but in order
to adore Him.

....

Johann A. Bengel

99

September 19

September 20

September 21

GOD'S PROMISES - MY KNOWLEDGE

OT *Isaiah 37; 38*   September 19   *Hebrews 4* NT

OT *Isaiah 39; 40*   September 20   *Psalm 106* Ps

SEP

OT *Isaiah 41; 42*   September 21   *Hebrews 5* NT

66

There is a book that accompanies us until the hour of our death. It teaches us to live; it teaches us to die.

....

Eduard Spranger

99

September 22

September 23

September 24

GOD'S PROMISES - MY KNOWLEDGE

OT *Isaiah 43; 44*   September 22   *Hebrews 6* NT

_____

OT *Isaiah 45; 46*   September 23   *Psalm 107* Ps

_____

SEP

OT *Isaiah 47; 48*   September 24   *Hebrews 7* NT

_____

> "
>
> Prayer is the breath of faith.
>
> ....
>
> Frank M. Hasel
>
> "

September 25

September 26

September 27

SEP

OT *Isaiah 49; 50*   September 25   *Hebrews 8* NT

OT *Isaiah 51; 52*   September 26   *Hebrews 9* NT

SEP

OT *Isaiah 53; 54*   September 27   *Psalms 108; 109* Ps

> The Bible is not an end in itself, but a means to bring men to an intimate and satisfying knowledge of God, that they may enter into Him, that they may delight in His Presence, may taste and know the inner sweetness of the very God Himself in the core and center of their hearts.

....

A. W. Tozer

September 28

September 29

September 30

OT *Isaiah 55; 56*　　　　　September 28　　　　　*Hebrews 10* NT

OT *Isaiah 57; 58*　　　　　September 29　　　　　*Hebrews 11* NT

SEP

OT *Isaiah 59; 60*　　　　　September 30　　　　　*Psalms 110; 111* Ps

MORE THOUGHTS

10 SUGGESTIONS
for Encouragement

SEPTEMBER

*Practical suggestions for prayer and proven suggestions
to think about your faith life*

In 1 Thessalonians 5:11 the apostle Paul writes, "And so encourage one another and help one another, just as you are now doing" (GNT). Encouraging words lift up. Encouragement that we give to others helps to make our burdens lighter. To encourage one another is God's way to be there for one another. Here are ten specific suggestions for how you can encourage another person.

1. Write an encouraging text message, a card, or—even better—a real letter.

2. Tell an encouraging experience (e.g., how God has helped you in your life or how you overcame a difficult situation and how your trust in God increased because of it). Your personal testimony can encourage someone.

3. Be an encouragement for someone simply by being there and being close, even if you don't have answers to all the questions and if you don't understand everything.

4. Tell the other person why you value him or her and that you are happy that he or she exists.

5. Where possible, take care of some of the difficulties the other person has (e.g., by helping him or her financially or by taking care of specific needs).

6. Be happy with others when they are successful, and express your happiness to them.

SEP

7. Stand up for your neighbor or your brother or sister in Christ and support them when they are discouraged and feel lonely.

8. Pray for someone by name and let them know what specifically you are praying for.

9. Remind the other person of a precious Bible promise.

10. Remind the other person how God has led in the past. That opens up encouraging perspectives because we have nothing to fear for the future except as we forget how God has led us in the past.

"As you have opportunity, speak to the workers; speak words that will be a strength and an inspiration. We are altogether too indifferent in regard to one another. Too often we forget that our fellow laborers are in need of strength and cheer. In times of special perplexity and burden, take care to assure them of your interest and sympathy. While you try to help them by your prayers, let them know that you do it. Send along the line God's message to His workers: 'Be strong and of a good courage.' Joshua 1:6."[1]

---

1. Ellen G. White, *Testimony Treasures,* vol. 3, p. 174.

The Bible is full of encouragement. If we are in a difficult situation when we are sad and desperate, we need encouragement. God has encouraging thoughts about us and pursues only one goal—to give us peace, hope, and a future.

"For I know the plans I have for you," declares the LORD, *"plans to prosper you and not to harm you, plans to give you hope and a future."*

Jeremiah 29:11

LONGING FOR GOD

· · · · · · · · · · · · · · · · · ·

PRAYER JOURNAL
&
BIBLE JOURNAL

OCTOBER

✕

> **"**
>
> If we worship God only in good times, then we have to ask ourselves if we have really understood the meaning of worship.
>
> ....
> Hans Peter Royer
>
> **"**

October 1

October 2

October 3

OT *Isaiah 61; 62*   October 1   *Hebrews 12* NT

_____   _____
_____   _____
_____   _____
_____   _____
_____   _____
_____   _____
_____   _____

OT *Isaiah 63; 64*   October 2   *Hebrews 13* NT

_____   _____
_____   _____
_____   _____
_____   _____
_____   _____
_____   _____
_____   _____

OCT

OT *Isaiah 65; 66*   October 3   *John 1* NT

_____   _____
_____   _____
_____   _____
_____   _____
_____   _____
_____   _____
_____   _____

66

We will criticize
the Bible as long as
we do not criticize
ourselves.

....
Peter Hahne

99

October 4

October 5

October 6

OT *Jeremiah 1; 2*   October 4   *Psalms 112; 113* Ps

OT *Jeremiah 3; 4*   October 5   *John 2* NT

OCT

OT *Jeremiah 5; 6*   October 6   *John 3* NT

"

We always have the choice: complain, lament, blame— or getting up, believing, praying, acting.

....

Astrid Eichler

"

October 7

October 8

October 9

OT *Jeremiah 7; 8*　　　　October 7　　　　*Psalms 114; 115*　Ps

OT *Jeremiah 9; 10*　　　　October 8　　　　*John 4* NT

OCT

OT *Jeremiah 11; 12*　　　　October 9　　　　*John 5* NT

66

We know as little where we come from as we do where we are going or even what we are really supposed to be and do here: and we have nothing in our hands on which we can depend and with which we can comfort ourselves and still our hearts. But God has stilled our heart through His Scripture.

....

Matthias Claudius

99

October 10

October 11

October 12

OT *Jeremiah 13; 14*　　　　October 10　　　　*John 6* NT

OT *Jeremiah 15; 16*　　　　October 11　　　　*Psalm 116* Ps

OCT

OT *Jeremiah 17; 18*　　　　October 12　　　　*John 7* NT

> 66
>
> To love God means to enjoy Him, to gladly think of Him, to gladly pray to Him.
>
> . . . .
>
> Dietrich Bonhoeffer
>
> 99

October 13

October 14

October 15

OT *Jeremiah 19; 20*   October 13   *John 8* NT

OT *Jeremiah 21; 22*   October 14   *Psalms 117; 118* Ps

OCT

OT *Jeremiah 23; 24*   October 15   *John 9* NT

"

A thorough
knowledge of
the Bible is worth
more than a college
education.

Theodore Roosevelt

"

October 16

October 17

October 18

OCT

GOD'S PROMISES - MY KNOWLEDGE

OT *Jeremiah 25; 26*   October 16   *John 10* NT

_____

_____

_____

_____

_____

_____

_____

OT *Jeremiah 27; 28*   October 17   *John 11* NT

_____

_____

_____

_____

_____

_____

_____

OCT

OT *Jeremiah 29–31*   October 18   *Psalm 119:1–24* Ps

_____

_____

_____

_____

_____

_____

_____

66

Pray until you can pray; pray to be helped to pray and do not give up praying because you cannot pray. For it is when you think you cannot pray; that is when you are praying.

....
C. H. Spurgeon

99

October 19

October 20

October 21

OT *Jeremiah 32; 33*   October 19   *John 12* NT

OT *Jeremiah 34; 35*   October 20   *John 13* NT

OCT

OT *Jeremiah 36; 37*   October 21   *Psalm 119:25–48* Ps

MY PRAISE · MY THANKS · MY PRAYERS

> **"**
>
> The promises in the
> Bible are a blank
> check from God.
>
> ·········
>
> Peter Hahne
>
> **"**

October 22

October 23

October 24

OT *Jeremiah 38; 39*   October 22   *John 14* NT

OT *Jeremiah 40; 41*   October 23   *John 15* NT

OT *Jeremiah 42; 43*   October 24   *John 16* NT

OCT

October 25 Thank you for sending help. Thank you for my husband, thank you for mental clarity returning. Please keep and protect my husband. Please God help him to excel at his work. Help him to study. Help him to do well in his mental health. Help our marriage to be strong. God please forgive me. I feel really down about what happened w/ JJ mom. Please God. Help me to move past this.

October 26

October 27

OT *Jeremiah 44–46* October 25 *Psalm 119:49–72* Ps

God is going to punish Israel for its wrong doing. He specifically addresses wifes/women. He will preserve in the end a remnant but they will not go wholly unpunished. God just don't leave me. I feel like I deserve to be punished but I'm scared. It says don't be afraid.

It is good for me that I have been afflicted that I might learn your statues. v.72 v.66 Teach me judgement and knowledge. For I believe your commandments.

OT *Jeremiah 47; 48* October 26 *John 17* NT

OT *Jeremiah 49; 50* October 27 *John 18* NT

> No one is so highly educated or so uneducated that he could afford to do without the Bible.

Paul W. von Keppler

October 28

October 29

October 30

October 31

GOD'S PROMISES - MY KNOWLEDGE

OT *Jeremiah 51; 52*   October 28   *Psalm 119:73–96* Ps

OT *Lamentations 1; 2*   October 29   *John 19* NT

OT *Lamentations 3–5*   October 30   *John 20* NT

OCT

OT *Ezekiel 1*   October 31   *John 21* NT

MORE THOUGHTS

....

SUGGESTIONS
for Praying Together

OCTOBER

✕

*Practical suggestions for prayer and proven suggestions
to think about your faith life*

The following thoughts are meant as suggestions for praying together with a prayer partner. Some of the ideas can also be used for praying with a spouse or a friend.

Jesus Christ promised in Matthew 18:19, 20: "If two of you agree on earth concerning anything that they ask, it will be done for them by My Father in heaven. For where two or three are gathered together in My name, I am there in the midst of them" (NKJV).

✧ PRAYING TOGETHER CONNECTS US ✧

Praying together can lead to the most intensive and meaningful moments in a relationship. Praying together connects you with your partner on a deep spiritual level. It binds you together. It is a wellspring of encouragement and an invaluable expression of mutual support. It helps us to carry responsibility jointly. By praying together, the burden of a task is shared and thereby becomes lighter. I realize that I am not alone. Shared joy becomes greater joy by praying together. It is a sign of appreciation and gives my attention to the other person. It expresses sympathy and shows that I am caring. It is an expression of mutual trust. In short, it is an inestimable blessing for every relationship.

In order that this positive effect can really unfold and possibly make your prayer partner more receptive to the idea of praying together, several things need to be observed:

Never use prayer with your spouse or friend to express concealed criticism of the other. Do not use this joint prayer time as a tactic to apply subtle pressure or to express reproach. It is an abuse of prayer when you use it to express your dissatisfaction with the other person. Nobody likes concealed hints and reproaches. Such prayers repel. They cause hearts to close and result in an increasing unwillingness to pray together.

Pray *with* your friend or spouse, not *about* him or her. It is very easy to create the impression that you are preaching at the other person in your prayer. As long as your partner has not specifically asked for your prayer support in a concrete area where he or she needs help, it is wise to bring these things to God in your private prayer, not when you pray together.

OCT

Not everyone is used to praying together. Maybe your prayer partner, your friend, your spouse has never had the opportunity to observe a good example of praying together. Maybe they have had bad experiences with other people praying together. If your prayer partner is hesitant, don't push him or her! Be gentle. Be patient. That sounds simple but can become a big challenge when your own desire for praying together is strong.

Maybe your friend or spouse is willing to pray with you but finds it difficult to fully open up in prayer. Often greater trust in other areas also leads to greater openness when praying together. Ask God in your own private (!) prayer to give you wisdom and creativity to know how to increase mutual trust.

Pray for the other person. Pray for specific things and areas in which he or she is seeking help. Pray in such a way that the other person is encouraged and comforted by your prayer.

Let the other person know that *you* appreciate his or her prayers and need them for specific situations. For instance, you can say, "I would really appreciate it if you would pray for me today—even throughout the day. I am afraid of . . ." Or, "I need prayer protection when I go to this place . . ." That opens the opportunity to later share how things went and it can result in thanking God in prayer together or asking for His continued help.

Mealtimes often provide opportunities to pray together. For example, the family can hold hands before the meal and bring up a mutual prayer request: "Today we can thank God that He helped Mary during her test." Or, "Today we want to pray for good results tomorrow when John goes to the doctor to have his physical exam and for wisdom and skill in his health treatment."

In a family with children, it is sometimes easier for the parents to pray together with the children.

In our busy life it is sometimes important to plan for specific times to pray together. Talk to your friend or spouse about possible times you can pray together. Pray to find a suitable time. Where possible in a family, you can reserve a few minutes for praying together in the morning before or after breakfast or in the evening before going to bed.

Remind the other person through a friendly text message that you are praying for him or her.

Sometimes it is only possible to pray together by telephone or video chat. That is a fabulous opportunity to stay in prayer contact even across great distances and to let the other person know that you are praying for him or her.

Read an encouraging Bible text before you pray together. Remind yourself of God's attributes and abilities and thank Him for what He has done already and is willing to do in the future.

OCT

LONGING FOR GOD

PRAYER JOURNAL
&
BIBLE JOURNAL

NOVEMBER

66

It is much easier
to pray for a bore
than to go visit
him.

....
C. S. Lewis

99

November 1

November 2

November 3

NOV

OT *Ezekiel 2; 3*　　　　　　**November 1**　　　　　*Psalm 119:97–120* Ps

OT *Ezekiel 4; 5*　　　　　　**November 2**　　　　　　*James 1* NT

OT *Ezekiel 6; 7*　　　　　　**November 3**　　　　　　*James 2* NT

NOV

66

There is a book
that many people
do not know even
though they have
memorized it.

. . . .

Marie Freifrau
von Ebner-Eschenbach

99

November 4

November 5

November 6

OT *Ezekiel 8; 9*   November 4   *Psalm 119:121–144* Ps

_____   _____
_____   _____
_____   _____
_____   _____
_____   _____
_____   _____
_____   _____

OT *Ezekiel 10; 11*   November 5   *James 3* NT

_____   _____
_____   _____
_____   _____
_____   _____
_____   _____
_____   _____
_____   _____

OT *Ezekiel 12; 13*   November 6   *James 4* NT

NOV

_____   _____
_____   _____
_____   _____
_____   _____
_____   _____
_____   _____
_____   _____

> "
>
> Intercession usually means prayer on behalf of others. It is the greatest single ministy, in my opinion, that the Christian is privileged to have.
>
> ....
>
> Gordon MacDonald
>
> "

November 7

November 8

November 9

OT *Ezekiel 14; 15*   November 7   *James 5* NT

OT *Ezekiel 16; 17*   November 8   *Psalm 119:145–176* Ps

OT *Ezekiel 18; 19*   November 9   *1 Peter 1* NT

NOV

66

The greatest tragedy of life is not unanswered prayer, but unoffered prayer.

....

F. B. Meyer

99

November 10

November 11

November 12

OT *Ezekiel 20; 21*   November 10   *1 Peter 2* NT

OT *Ezekiel 22; 23*   November 11   *Psalms 120; 122* Ps

OT *Ezekiel 24; 25*   November 12   *1 Peter 3* NT

NOV

❝

It is not that our prayers are not answered but that we do not accept the answers.

....

Kosti Tolonen

❞

November 13

November 14

November 15

OT *Ezekiel 26; 27*　　November 13　　*1 Peter 4* NT

OT *Ezekiel 28; 29*　　November 14　　*1 Peter 5* NT

OT *Ezekiel 30; 31*　　November 15　　*Psalms 123–125* Ps

NOV

"

The one who has
lost his God can
find Him again
in the Bible; and
the one who has
never known Him,
finds there that
the breath of God
breathes on him.

·········

Heinrich Heine

"

November 16

November 17

November 18

OT *Ezekiel 32; 33*　　　　　November 16　　　　　*2 Peter 1* NT

OT *Ezekiel 34; 35*　　　　　November 17　　　　　*2 Peter 2* NT

OT *Ezekiel 36; 37*　　　　　November 18　　　　　*Psalms 126–128* Ps

NOV

66

It is almost unbelievable how far we will go to avoid obeying God. We call Jesus "Lord" and beg Him to rejuvenate our souls, but we are careful to do not the things He says. When faced with a sin, a confession or moral alteration in our life, we find it much easier to pray half a night than to obey God.

....

A. W. Tozer

99

NOV

November 19

November 20

November 21

OT *Ezekiel 38; 39* **November 19** *2 Peter 3* NT

OT *Ezekiel 40; 41* **November 20** *1 John 1* NT

OT *Ezekiel 42; 43* **November 21** *1 John 2* NT

NOV

66

Whoever does not read the Scripture with a praying heart that is turned to God leaves an abundant table empty, feeble, and emaciated regardless of how much the head may have gleaned.

....

Gerhard Tersteegen

99

November 22

November 23

November 24

NOV

OT *Ezekiel 44; 45*　　　November 22　　　*Psalms 129–131* Ps

OT *Ezekiel 46; 47*　　　November 23　　　*1 John 3* NT

OT *Ezekiel 48*　　　November 24　　　*1 John 4* NT

NOV

66

Prayer means to
have secrets with
God.

. . . .

Paul Deitenbeck

99

November 25

November 26

November 27

OT *Daniel 1–3* **November 25** *Psalms 132–134* Ps

OT *Daniel 4; 5* **November 26** *1 John 5* NT

OT *Daniel 6; 7* **November 27** *2 John* NT

NOV

MY PRAISE · MY THANKS · MY PRAYERS

66

Intercessory prayer
isn't rocket science.
It acknowledges
our inability and
God's ability.

·········

Max Lucado

99

November 28

November 29

November 30

OT *Daniel 8; 9*   **November 28**   *3 John* NT

OT *Daniel 10–12*   **November 29**   *Psalms 135; 136* Ps

OT *Hosea 1; 2*   **November 30**   *Jude* NT

NOV

MORE THOUGHTS

....

PRAYERS
for Missionaries

N O V E M B E R

*Practical suggestions for prayer and proven suggestions
to think about your faith life*

Missionaries are people who, from a spiritual viewpoint, fight at the front line. Frequently they find themselves in special situations and circumstances and are confronted with great challenges that require the support of our prayers. The following suggestions are to help us pray specifically for situations that occur primarily in foreign countries.[1] If you don't know a missionary in a foreign land, get in contact with your pastor or your church leadership to learn about specific people for whom you can pray, and try to get in contact with them. It will inspire your faith and spark more interest in missionary work.

However, there are missionaries in our own latitudes also. Adapt the suggestions to their unique circumstances (e.g., when they go from door to door to tell people about God or to disperse Christian literature). If you know a missionary by name, you may insert the name into the prayer.

Imagine that you have to learn to speak and read a new language. Ask God that He will help _____ to learn the language of the people well enough so that they will understand the gospel he/she is bringing to them. Ask God that even though his/her language may be imperfect, God's love will always shine through his/her speech and actions.

Imagine you live in a foreign culture with habits and customs that are not familiar to you. Pray for sensitivity and that _____ will correctly understand and evaluate the habits and customs of the new culture. Pray that he/she will treat others with humility, wisdom, and respect so that they will not be repelled.

Imagine you work for weeks, months, even years without much visible success. Pray for endurance, alertness, and patience when results do not happen as quickly as desired. Pray that _____ will stay faithful to God in spite of obstacles and slow progress.

Imagine you live in a remote region where you have to depend on fellow workers and their support. Maybe they have to go shopping for you, reorder supplies, and take care of a multitude of other needs. Pray for a trusting and dependable interaction in these everyday matters.

NOV

Imagine you live in a country where the available food is unfamiliar and hygiene is lacking. Pray that the food _____ eats agrees with him/her, that he/she will get sufficient strength from it, that clean water is available, and that he/she can stay healthy.

Imagine you have to raise and educate your children in an unfamiliar culture and surroundings where there are no public schools or church schools. Pray for wisdom, patience, love, balance, and the necessary support for this important task. Pray that the children understand that they are also witnesses for God and that they will find good friends.

In unfamiliar surroundings and surrounded by a foreign language, in the midst of a new culture and without local friends, it is easy to be lonesome. Pray that _____ will not become discouraged. Pray for wisdom and creativity to show _____ that others pray for him/her and that he/she is not forgotten.

Missionaries often travel and from time to time face dangerous situations. Sometimes they meet dangerous or poisonous animals, and sometimes they are in danger through people. Pray for special protection by God's angels wherever he/she goes. Pray that _____ will know that the Lord has not given him/her "a spirit of fear, but of power and of love and of a sound mind" (2 Timothy 1:7, NKJV).

Missionaries are also confronted with spiritual darkness and the work of demonic powers. Pray for spiritual courage and assurance in the face of these obstacles and especially for protection from all evil so that _____ will find that Jesus is truly victorious.

Imagine you face daily demands to fill urgent needs of others (medical, pastoral, spiritual, needs of your own family and of fellow workers, etc.). In the midst of this endless giving, it is easy to neglect one's own devotional time. Pray that God will keep the desire for communion with Him alive in the heart of _____ and that he/she will take time for spiritual refreshment and physical fitness. Ask God to keep the vision for this work alive.

Missionaries often depend on financial support from others. Ask God for people who are willing to back missionaries. Ask God for sufficient funds to support the work.

Some missionaries are married, others single. Pray that God will help _____ to be faithful in every respect to his/her spouse so that they can support each other. For single missionaries pray that God will help them to focus their undivided attention on God and His work. Also, ask God for people who will encourage them, support them, and include them in their family and their circle of friends.

Ask God for a peaceful relationship and open doors with local tribal leaders, chiefs, and responsible persons so that the good news can be spread without obstacles.

Ask God for wisdom on how you can tactfully establish contact with foreigners who are guests in your country and neighborhood in order to show them kindness and help. Once they have experienced your love and selfless support they might also open their hearts for the good news of Jesus Christ. Maybe there are immigrants, guest workers, students, or specialists in your area who are from countries where otherwise it would not be possible to preach the gospel. Maybe you can be an international missionary in your own neighborhood.

Ask God for more helpers because the harvest is plentiful, but the laborers are few (Matthew 9:37).

---

1. The following suggestions for prayer needs were taken from the website of Adventist Frontier Missions (AFM) (http://www.afmonline.org). AFM is a mission organization that works especially in areas and among people groups where there are no Christians yet.

LONGING FOR GOD

PRAYER JOURNAL
&
BIBLE JOURNAL

DECEMBER

"

For most of us
the prayer in
Gethsemane is
the only model.
Removing
mountains can
wait.

....

C. S. Lewis

"

December 1

December 2

December 3

DEC

OT *Hosea 3–6*   December 1   *Revelation 1* NT

OT *Hosea 7; 8*   December 2   *Psalms 137; 138* Ps

OT *Hosea 9; 10*   December 3   *Revelation 2* NT

DEC

"

When I try, I fail.
When I trust, He
succeeds.

....

Corrie ten Boom

"

December 4

December 5

December 6

DEC

OT *Hosea 11; 12*   December 4   *Revelation 3* NT

OT *Hosea 13; 14*   December 5   *Revelation 4* NT

OT *Joel 1; 2*   December 6   *Psalm 139* Ps

66

The gate of heaven is to be opened only in one way, by the very earnest use of the knocker of prayer.

. . . .

C. H. Spurgeon

99

December 7

December 8

December 9

OT *Joel 3*   December 7   *Revelation 5* NT

OT *Amos 1; 2*   December 8   *Revelation 6* NT

OT *Amos 3; 4*   December 9   *Psalms 140; 141* Ps

DEC

66

Do not pray for easy lives. Pray to be stronger men. Do not pray for tasks equal to your powers, pray for powers equal to your task.

....
Phillips Brooks

99

December 10

December 11

December 12

OT *Amos 5; 6*   December 10   *Revelation 7* NT

OT *Amos 7; 8*   December 11   *Revelation 8* NT

OT *Amos 9*   December 12   *Revelation 9* NT

DEC

> We have to pray with our eyes on God, not on the difficulties.

....

Oswald Chambers

December 13

December 14

December 15

DEC

OT *Obadiah*   December 13   *Psalms 142; 143* Ps

OT *Jonah 1; 2*   December 14   *Revelation 10* NT

OT *Jonah 3; 4*   December 15   *Revelation 11* NT

DEC

66

The devil often laughs when we work, but he trembles when we pray.

. . . .

Corrie ten Boom

99

December 16

December 17

December 18

DEC

OT *Micah 1–3*   December 16   *Psalm 144*   Ps

OT *Micah 4; 5*   December 17   *Revelation 12* NT

OT *Micah 6; 7*   December 18   *Revelation 13* NT

DEC

66

Prayer makes room
for the voice of God
to tell you that you
are beloved. When
you do not pray,
you run around and
beg for affirmation.
And then you are
not free.

....
Henri Nouwen

99

December 19

December 20

December 21

DEC

OT *Nahum 1–3*   December 19   *Revelation 14* NT

OT *Habakkuk 1–3*   December 20   *Psalm 145* Ps

OT *Zephaniah 1–3*   December 21   *Revelation 15* NT

DEC

"

By most people
God is seen as a
sort of customer
service which can be
contacted through
prayer instead of the
telephone.

....

Ilona Bodden

"

December 22

December 23

December 24

OT *Haggai 1; 2*   December 22   *Revelation 16* NT

OT *Zechariah 1; 2*   December 23   *Psalms 146; 147* Ps

OT *Zechariah 3; 4*   December 24   *Revelation 17* NT

DEC

MY PRAISE · MY THANKS · MY PRAYERS

66

For twenty-eight years, since I became a doctor, I have now constantly read and preached the Bible; and yet I have not exhausted it but find something new in it every day.

....

Martin Luther

99

December 25

December 26

December 27

DEC

OT *Zechariah 5; 6*   December 25   *Revelation 18* NT

OT *Zechariah 7; 8*   December 26   *Revelation 19* NT

OT *Zechariah 9; 10*   December 27   *Psalm 148* Ps

DEC

December 28 Thank you that JJ got home safely thank you for your care and love. I praise your faithfulness. Lord please help me accept my life. Forgive me for my covetousness and all my inbred faults and chosen faults. Help me to love and ~~Donate~~ see my children. God make up for all I lack. I love you.

December 29 Dear Heavenly Father, I messed up. I have tried Lord. Now please help me find the people for my children. I can't keep doing this. Forgive my sins thank you. I'm sorry for how I am. God I'm having a hard time. I have never grown. I am stuck a loser.

December 30

December 31

OT *Zechariah 11; 12* December 28 the neccessibly of our country *Revelation 20* NT

Prophecy against
Shepherds/predictions
about Jesus even down
to the 30 pieces of
silver

God Judges the whole world.
Please God help me fear you.
Help me respect you and obey you
thank you for destroying sin.
Please help met friends/family not to
be destroyed. Bless Elizay Lauren, Morrie
Matthew, Fernanda, Brody,

OT *Zechariah 13; 14* December 29 *Revelation 21* NT

Gods blood cleanses
we are only made clean
by Jesus.

Nothing that defiles will
be in Heaven. Those written in
the Lambs book of life and
God Himself will be there.

OT *Malachi 1; 2* December 30 *Psalms 149; 150* Ps

OT *Malachi 3; 4* December 31 *Revelation 22* NT

MORE THOUGHTS

························

SUGGESTIONS *for* INTERCESSION

DECEMBER

✕

Practical suggestions for prayer and proven suggestions
to think about your faith life

With our limited intellect we may not understand all the interaction between God's omniscience, His omnipotence, His love, and our intercessory prayer. But the following principles are clearly expressed in the Bible.

INTERCESSION IS AN IMPORTANT ASPECT IN THE LIFE OF BELIEVERS

In the Bible intercession is an important part of the service of those who preach the Word of God.

> Moreover, as for me, far be it from me that I should sin against the LORD in ceasing to pray for you; but I will teach you the good and the right way (1 Samuel 12:23, NKJV).

The apostle Paul encourages us to pray not only for believers but for all people.

> Therefore I exhort first of all that supplications, prayers, intercessions, and giving of thanks be made for all men, for kings and all who are in authority, that we may lead a quiet and peaceable life in all godliness and reverence. For this is good and acceptable in the sight of God our Savior, who desires all men to be saved and to come to the knowledge of the truth (1 Timothy 2:1–4, NKJV).

In our intercession we direct our will and our prayers to God's possibilities. I bring a person or an item to God—making this request in the spirit of Jesus—and in faith I count on God's unlimited power and possibilities. It is not a matter of bringing my own preferences to God to demand of God to act according to my wishes. Rather, when I intercede, I align with God and His desire and ask for that which will glorify Him and bring honor to His name.

DEC

❧ JESUS IS OUR EXAMPLE IN INTERCESSION ❧

Jesus observed times of prayer (Mark 1:35; Luke 11:1) and prayed intensely for His disciples (John 17).

> I pray for them. I do not pray for the world but for those whom You have given Me, for they are Yours. . . . Holy Father, keep through Your name those whom You have given Me, that they may be one as We are. . . . I do not pray that You should take them out of the world, but that You should keep them from the evil one. . . . Sanctify them by Your truth. Your word is truth. . . .
>
> I do not pray for these alone, but also for those who will believe in Me through their word; that they all may be one. . . .
>
> Father, I desire that they also whom You gave Me may be with Me where I am (John 17:9–24, NKJV).

It was important for Jesus to pray for His followers. His example spurs us on.

❧ THROUGH INTERCESSION ❧ I TAKE PART IN GOD'S WORK

In Ephesians 6:18, 19, Paul writes:

> Praying always with all prayer and supplication in the Spirit, being watchful to this end with all perseverance and supplication for all the saints—and for me, that utterance may be given to me, that I may open my mouth boldly to make known the mystery of the gospel (NKJV; cf. Philippians 4:6).

In Colossians 1:9–11 Paul describes how he intercedes for the believers in Colossae:

> For this reason we also, since the day we heard it, do not cease to pray for you, and to ask that you may be filled with the knowledge of His will in all wisdom and spiritual understanding;

that you may walk worthy of the Lord, fully pleasing Him, being fruitful in every good work and increasing in the knowledge of God; strengthened with all might, according to His glorious power, for all patience and longsuffering with joy (NKJV).

The early church was also united in intercession. In Acts 12:5 we read that constant prayer was offered by the church when Peter was in prison.

∽ INTERCESSION CHANGES US ∿

For Paul and the first Christians it was a privilege to daily come before God in intercession. Today we, too, can pray for one another and ask for God's help. We can do that together with other believers in the church, alone at home, or while being on the road. Yes, even while being in a hospital bed or sitting in a wheelchair it is possible to pray for others. Prayer unites us—even across large distances.

Intercession changes things—in many ways. First of all, it changes the one who is praying. My prayer does not bring God down to me; it lifts me up into God's presence. It gives me new insight into His possibilities. It opens my heart to the needs of other people. It lets me have a part in God's yearning for us lost sinners and in His workings in this world.

However, intercessory prayer also changes the lives of others. Even though humanly it is not possible to explain how God works, we know, based on the Word of God and through faith experiences, that through prayer God can supernaturally work on the hearts and minds of other people and intervene in situations and processes. It is a fact that God desires that by faith we will ask great things of Him. Our prayers provide Him with the opportunity to reveal Himself in mighty ways.

Yet, in all our prayers God still remains sovereign. In His love and wisdom He does what He knows is right and best.

It is a great blessing to pray for others. Try it out. It is worth it!

DEC

Worry is blind, and cannot discern the future; but Jesus sees the end from the beginning. In every difficulty He has His way prepared to bring relief. Our heavenly Father has a thousand ways to provide for us, of which we know nothing. Those who accept the one principle of making the service and honor of God supreme will find perplexities vanish, and a plain path before their feet.

Ellen G. White, *The Desire of Ages*, p. 330

PRAYER EMPHASES
FOR EACH DAY OF THE WEEK

*Now, my brothers, I am going to ask you, for the sake of Christ himself
and for the love we bear each other in the Spirit, to stand
behind me in earnest prayer to God on my behalf.*
—Paul in Romans 15:30 (Phillips)

*If My people who are called by My name will humble themselves, and pray
and seek My face, and turn from their wicked ways, then I will hear from
heaven, and will forgive their sin and heal their land.*
—God in 2 Chronicles 7:14 (NKJV)

The following pages offer suggestions to pray regularly on each day of the week for specific persons or prayer requests. Each day of the week has a special prayer emphasis on which the prayers for this day are concentrated. In this way, the daily prayer time can be more focused.[1]

*At all times and in all places, in all sorrows and in all afflictions, when the outlook
seems dark and the future perplexing, and we feel helpless and alone, the Comforter
will be sent in answer to the prayer of faith. Circumstances may separate us from
every earthly friend; but no circumstance, no distance, can separate us from the
heavenly Comforter. Wherever we are, wherever we may go, He is always at our
right hand to support, sustain, uphold, and cheer.*
—Ellen G. White, *The Desire of Ages*, p. 669

⌢ PRAY FOR PERSONAL GUIDANCE ⌢

Your spiritual renewal and revival starts with you. Ask God today to give you clarity in important areas of your own life. In which areas of your life do you need wisdom to know how to act correctly? Think about your private life, your spiritual life, your friendships, your family/marriage, your work, your education or training. Where do you need courage to make changes that are in harmony with the will of God? Where does your trust in God and His word need to grow so that you can believe that God's will, as revealed in the Holy Scriptures, is good for your life? List specific personal prayer requests, and consider concrete steps for how to proceed in those areas to reach your goals. Entrust to God your innermost yearnings and wishes, as well as your secret apprehensions and fears. Ask God for courage to view these very personal requests in the light of His Word. Allow God to lead in your life, and make all areas of your life available to God's guidance (Romans 12:1, 2).

∽ PRAY FOR PERSONAL GUIDANCE ∾

Date	Prayer Request	Answer to Prayer

∾ PRAY FOR YOUR FAMILY ∾

Pray for every member of your family (father, mother, son, daughter, brother, sister). If you are married, extended family members also belong to your family (e.g., in-laws, possibly grandchildren [you will find some practical suggestions on how to pray for others in May's chapter]). If your family grows through birth, marriage, or adoption, add the new members to your list. Each week bring to God each member of your family. Consider situations in which your family members particularly need support, help, wisdom, guidance, strength, confidence, courage, and comfort. Ask God to give them what they need and that He will show you how He can use you to be a blessing to them. Ask God that He will lead each individual member of your family step by step closer to Jesus Christ. And thank God for what He has already done in their lives and is still doing.

PRAY FOR YOUR FAMILY

Date	Prayer Request	Answer to Prayer

❧ PRAY FOR YOUR NEIGHBOR, YOUR TOWN ❧

Jeremiah 29:7 contains some of God's instructions for the Jews in Babylonian captivity; the principles in this verse still apply to us today: "Work for the good of the cities. . . . Pray to me on their behalf, because if they are prosperous, you will be prosperous too" (GNT). Included in the people of your city are also the people who live near you, with whom you are working, with whom you go to school or study, whom you meet while shopping, who live in your suburb, and so on. Think about the needs of the people in your area and how they can best be helped according to God's will. Ask God to show you kind and helpful ways to make contact with your neighbors, fellow men and women, and colleagues so that you can win their trust and friendship and in that way "work for the good of the cities."

❧ PRAY FOR YOUR NEIGHBOR, YOUR TOWN ❧

Date	Prayer Request	Answer to Prayer

❧ PRAY FOR YOUR COUNTRY ❧

The apostle Paul writes, "First of all, then, I urge that petitions, prayers, requests, and thanksgivings be offered to God for all people; for kings and all others who are in authority, that we may live a quiet and peaceful life with all reverence toward God and with proper conduct. This is good and it pleases God our Savior" (1 Timothy 2:1–3, GNT). Too rarely do we pray for the land in which we live and the men and women in our government. Pray for the mayor of your town or city, for council members, the president, and members of the assembly and congress. Pray for important national concerns and interests and that believers can practice their faith in peace and freedom. Ask God for wisdom and creativity to know how you can be a blessing to your country according to God's will.

PRAY FOR YOUR COUNTRY

Date	Prayer Request	Answer to Prayer

∽ PRAY FOR WORLD MISSIONS ∾

Pray for the advancement of world missions. Today more Christians are persecuted than ever before. Even today, there are many, many millions of people and thousands of people groups who have never (!) heard of Jesus Christ. The time for world missions is not past. Pray especially for people who live in the 10/40 window (between 10 degrees north and 40 degrees north latitude) that stretches from West Africa to East Asia. That is the seat of great world religions, and few people from this part of the world have been reached with the gospel. In our own country we have immigrants, refugees, guest workers, specialists, and students from these regions. In their new surroundings, they are often grateful for gestures of friendliness and appreciate practical help and a friendly smile. Maybe in your area God will bring you into contact with people in whose countries the gospel cannot easily be proclaimed. Ask God for love for these people and for wisdom on how you can tactfully relate to them. Think about how you can best win their friendship and at the right time give them a Bible or other relevant literature in their mother tongue. You can find suggestions for specific concerns for missionaries in the November chapter.

∼ PRAY FOR WORLD MISSIONS ∼

Date	Prayer Request	Answer to Prayer

∾ PRAY FOR LONELY, SICK, AND NEEDY PERSONS ∾

Surely you know people who, because of special circumstances, find themselves in a position where they need special prayers and practical help. Maybe there has been a death of a loved one. Maybe there is sickness or there are special needs or other challenges they face. Maybe they are lonely and discouraged. Maybe they lost all their possessions through a natural disaster or war. Maybe they suffer pain or have to come to grips with a difficult prognosis for their illness. Maybe they don't know where to turn because they have lost their job or had to leave familiar surroundings. Find out which concrete challenges these people face, and find practical ways to help and support them. These people need your prayers and are often very grateful for kindness and practical help.

PRAY FOR LONELY, SICK, AND NEEDY PERSONS

Date	Prayer Request	Answer to Prayer

∽ PRAY FOR GOD'S CHURCH ∾

Focus your prayers on your church. Start with the local congregation. For example, pray for your pastor/minister, the elders, the teachers, the youth leaders, the outreach leaders, the deacons and deaconesses, the church school teachers, and others in positions of leadership. Also, include in your prayers the spouses and children of these people. Pray for members of your local church who are in special need of prayer support. Pray for the president and secretaries of your local conference, union, and division. Finally, pray for the worldwide church and its leaders. Pray that the elected leaders act faithfully according to God's will in all areas, that their personal relationship with Jesus stays alive, and that they are open to God's leading. Pray that they will have wisdom to lead the church in the right way, that they will have the courage by faith to lead the way and make decisions that are in accordance with God's will, even if they might be unpopular. Pray that they and their families will have God's blessings and protection while they travel. Ask God to show you how you can actively support the church in its different concerns and how you can contribute constructively. The apostle Paul admonishes us, "Keep alert and never give up; pray always for all God's people" (Ephesians 6:18, GNT).

---

1. I have taken the ideas for these focused prayer emphases for each day of the week from Ridings, *The Pray! Prayer Journal*, 7–14. The order and structure of the prayer emphases were changed and rearranged, as well as some of the content.

∽ PRAY FOR GOD'S CHURCH ∾

Date	Prayer Request	Answer to Prayer